Bodies, Health, and Consciousness

A Guide to Living Successfully in
Your Body Through Rolfing® and Yoga

ROSIE SPIEGEL

SRG Publishing
San Carlos, California

Grateful acknowledgment is made for permission to reproduce the following material: *Ageless Body, Timeless Mind* by Deepak Chopra, M. D., copyright 1993 by Harmony Books; *Reversing Heart Disease* by Dean Ornish, M.D., copyright 1992 by Random House; *Job's Body* by Deane Juhan, copyright 1987 by Station Hill Press; *Yoga and Psychotherapy* by Rudolph Ballentine, M.D., Swami Ajaya, Ph.D., and Swami Rama, copyright 1976 by Himalayan International Institute of Yoga and Philosophy; *Peace, Love, and Healing* by Bernie Segal, M.D., copyright 1989 by Harper & Row; *Body, Self, and Soul* by Jack Lee Rosenberg, copyright 1985 by Humanics Limited; and *Awakening the Spine* by Vanda Scaravelli, copyright 1991 by HarperCollins.

SRG Publishing
P.O. Box 7230
San Carlos, CA 94070

Rolfing® is a service mark of the Rolf Institute in Boulder, Colorado.

FIRST EDITION

Designed by Larry Spiegel, Rosie Spiegel, Dave McLoughlin, and Janice McLoughlin
Cover design by Mark LaMirande
Illustrations by Rhonda Chase
Photographs by Larry Watson

LIBRARY OF CONGRESS CATALOGING-IN-PUBLICATION DATE

Spiegel, Rosie, 1953–

Bodies, Health, and Consciousness: a guide to living successfully in your body through Rolfing and yoga/ Rosie Spiegel

Includes bibliographical references:
1. Rolfing and body therapy. 2. Yoga. 3. Movement. 4. Health and healing.

ISBN 0-9637824-0-1

Library of Congress Catalog Card Number: 93-85598
Printed and bound in the United States
10 9 8 7 6 5 4 3 2

Also Written by Rosie Spiegel
Yoga for Rolfers, Movement Teachers, and Their Clients

This book is dedicated to my darling husband, Larry, whose love and faith in me will always be at the root of my success, and whose ability to pursue a vision makes for a thrilling and satisfying journey together.

ACKNOWLEDGMENTS

A heartfelt thanks and my love go to the following individuals, who had enough faith in me to purchase a book when it was still a twinkle in this author's eye. Their financial support was a critical factor in enabling me to see this project through to its completion. The names of these generous individuals are as follows:

Burton and Amelie Bank, my parents; Bernie and Marlene Brown; Michale Kilgroe and Pat Burbank; Oz and Debbi Crosby; Koen Kallop; Pearl Spiegel; Steven Tulkin and Sydney Kapchan; Colleen Cayes; Philip Heller; Vera DePas; Bill Laird; Mark and Hava Finkle; Bernice Baer; Buddy and Linda Kaufman; Karen Beainy; Ray Mrofka and Lucia Mirracci; James Goss and Pamela McConnell; Amado Padilla; Robert Kutler; Connie Dunham; Jennifer McKeowen; Lynn Garrell; Saskia A. Boissevain; Rob and Suzy Schamberg; Phyllis Light; Mike Strauch; Kathy Layden; Dan Somers; Irene Estelle; Lainie Demian; Michelle and Rory Glaubert; Joyce Shipley; Carol Allison; Phil Salyer and Ellen Masland Salyer; Linda Byrum; Linda Gerber; Kevin Finnegan; Kenne Zugman; and Roger Pierce.

*　*　*　*　*

This book is the result of a collaborative effort on the part of many dedicated and talented individuals. My thanks, love, and appreciation go to each of the following people for working with me to help make my vision become a reality.

Gordon Thompson, for recovering the manuscript after it was devoured by my computer; Philip Heller, Kathie Lester, Dana Bredemeyer, and John Campbell, for reading and critiquing the manuscript in its rudimentary form; George Quasha and Chuck Stein at Station Hill Press, for telling me this was an important book; Deane Juhan, for paving the way with *Job's Body* and for writing a beautiful Forward for this book; Larry Watson, for great photographs; Marilyn Perry and Glenn Fetsch, for being such good models; Rhonda Chase, for her beautiful illustrations; Barbara Fuller, for being the world's greatest editor; Kathy Kaiser for excellent proof reading; Arnold Mindell and Gael Ohlgren, for their generous endorsement of this project; Donald Moyer of Rodmell Press, for his professional critique of the manuscript and for his patience in answering production-related questions; Dave and Janice McLoughlin, for their computer knowledge, late nights, and technical support; Mark LaMirande for the gorgeous cover; my friends, teachers, and colleagues at the Rolf Institute, for challenging me and inspiring me to present my work; my children, Frosty and Molly, for an endless supply of love and affection for their hard-working, fun-loving mom; and my beautiful husband, Larry, who said all along that we could do this together, and do it well.

TABLE OF CONTENTS

FOREWORD

Bodies, Health, and Consciousness offers a penetrating insight into the thoughts and sensibilities of a highly skilled bodyworker as she confronts her own training, her self-development, current theories of health and recovery, and the practical therapeutic problems presented by her clients and students. Rosie Spiegel is a Rolfer and a yoga instructor, and she speaks passionately about these "alternative" approaches to physical and mental health; but she does not create an adversarial polemic with "traditional" theory and practice. Nor does she argue for the value of her own skills over other alternative methods of health care. Rather, she celebrates the strengths and pinpoints the weaknesses in a variety of points of view, and offers a positive theoretical and practical synthesis that combines the clear benefits and balances the shortcomings of each.

Ida Rolf was herself a long-time student and practitioner of yoga, and it was this personal experience, as much as her academic studies in physiology, that formed the basis of her innovative technique of therapeutic manipulation. She largely suppressed these "spiritual" and "Eastern" dimensions of her work in her public writing and teaching, fearful that they would compromise the acceptance of the scientific validity of her discoveries. Rosie does an admirable job bringing these hidden foundations of Rolfing to light, and in so doing she recovers valuable tools for all Rolfers to add to their training and practice. In a time when the intellectual hostilities Dr. Rolf feared have somewhat abated, Rosie has helped to bring her vision a step closer to full disclosure and completion.

The ostensible subjects of this book are Rolfing and yoga, but Rosie makes them emblematic of far more extensive themes and issues in bodywork and health care. Yoga is very old, and Rolfing is quite new; both of them are outside the bounds of the mainstream, and neither deserves to be. Bodywork in a wide variety of forms is emerging as the fastest-growing sector of alternatives to surgery, pharmaceuticals, and medical technology for a wide variety of ailments. The more that we can understand about the similarities and differences, strengths and weaknesses, of these approaches to health, the more successfully we can develop both their potentials and their public acceptance.

The core concept here is that Rolfing, yoga, and bodywork are education, not intervention, and that our own personal awareness of our internal conditions and options is the key to our successful development and resolution of crises. Rosie refers to the hands-on manipulative side of the work as the structural side of this educational process, and to yoga and movement as the functional side. Both are necessary for the creation and maintenance of optimal health and activity. The hands-on part is the more passively received, instructional part of the education; the yoga and movement part is the more active, exploratory, self-directed part. As in every truly educational process, both "lecture" and "homework," absorbing information from the "teacher" and personally engaging in creative problem solving, must have equal weight.

The goal is not merely to fix what is currently wrong, but to bring forth a client's own sense of personal responsibility for his or her health and growth. Every wound and disability is an opportunity for the client to engage, observe, and arrive at a new and more successful understanding of how his or her organism works and what impact his or her habits and decisions have upon it. Nor is the end result the final achievement of some static model of perfect posture or authoritatively defined optimal function. "Holding correct posture," says Rosie, "is an oxymoron." And optimal function is properly, for human beings, a creative and open-ended process. The teaching and learning described in this book are precisely the insights and the strategies for letting go of limiting models and for endlessly exploring the ever-renewed growing edge of our sense of the optimum. This is not merely health care: this is engagement in personal evolution. And coupled with the other branches of education and medicine, its results will not be merely to return us to a familiar functional norm after injury or illness, but to astonish us with possibilities and capacities we never dreamed we could own.

Deane Juhan, author of *Job's Body*

INTRODUCTION

I have learned quite a bit over the years about the compatibility of yoga and Rolfing. As two excellent and complementary disciplines, yoga and Rolfing, done in conjunction, provide a means for opening and aligning the body that is as effective as any method available. Actually, we are discussing more than a methodology. A true immersion into either or both approaches becomes a way of life. The features of this lifestyle include a pervasive body awareness, a conscious determination to expand and relax the physical body, and the ability and commitment to handle and release the stress and tension that limit one's experience of optimal health.

Hatha yoga and Rolfing, or Structural Integration, mirror the values and philosophies of each other. In fact, when I teach Rolfers how to implement yoga in their practice, I emphasize that this is no departure from the work we already do. As a Rolfer and as a yoga instructor, I see the work with my clients and students in the same light. These are two parts of a greater whole. Individuals seek yoga for the same reasons they want to work with a Rolfer. The most common objectives that guide people to yoga and Rolfing are:

1. to gain relief from chronic or acute tension and pain
2. to increase flexibility and coordination
3. to improve posture and alignment
4. to learn to relax and obtain more body awareness
5. to offset the deleterious effects of aging
6. to release emotional blocks stored in the body
7. to have more energy and stamina
8. to find relief from breathing difficulties

9. to achieve optimal health through improved digestion, elimination, and circulation

10. to grow personally and spiritually and to gain self-awareness

Individuals realize these goals when they get Rolfed or when they become seriously involved in yoga. Richard Carlson, Ph.D., a certified Rolfer in Lafayette, California, and author of *Healers on Healing* and *For the Love of God*, recently commented on his experience of integrating yoga into his work with clients. "After working with yoga, I feel as if I were wearing a blindfold in my earlier years of Rolfing. Yoga takes the effort out of Rolfing for the client as well as the practitioner by gently exposing and releasing the specific muscles and tissues that need attention. Yoga allows a person to extend the ten sessions of Rolfing into a lifetime of peace and freedom."

In 1990, the Faculty Committee of the Rolf Institute unanimously approved my workshop, entitled "Yoga for Rolfers," to be taught to Rolfers who were already certified in the continuing education program of the Rolf training. The receptivity of the committee, which is very selective about what topics are included in the Rolfers' training track, is a statement of the compatibility of the two disciplines.

For more than twenty years, as I have studied bodies, health, and consciousness, I have paid considerable attention to the relationship between the body therapist and the client. I vividly recall in the mid- to late 1970s reading everything I could find on healing, bodywork, yoga, and spirituality. Catherine Ponder's work had a big influence on me; I referred frequently to her books in the classes I taught on healing and massage. *The Dynamic Laws of Healing* was one of my favorites. Her work was my first exposure to attitudinal healing, which is basically the mind's relation to resolving issues concerning health and disease. My heuristic education continues to be a vital source of information and a help in my personal growth.

The highlights of my training include certification through the Trager Institute. One book in particular, *Job's Body*, written by Trager Institute instructor Deane Juhan, had a profound impact on my work. That author's comments on pain and how to handle it in a professional context were consistent with the ideas I had been putting together for many years. Studying with Milton Trager also made a tremendous impression on me. His work is beautiful and gentle, and I don't believe he condones pain in any form. On the other hand, seasoned Rolfers (and Ida Rolf herself, when she was alive) have a greater capacity and willingness to dance in the arena where the client may be suffering because of the pressure or the intensity. I searched my soul, and continue to do so, to see where I stand on this sensitive issue. Although it is not my preference, I am willing for the work with my clients to be uncomfortable at times. But, I am completely unwilling to touch a client in any way that is not acceptable to him. If we are permitted to do work that may be confrontational, either emotionally or physically, then many doors open that might otherwise be closed. These questions have been a major consideration for me, having trained at the Trager Institute as well as at the Rolf Institute.

The client must feel safe. Trust is of paramount importance, especially when trust and safety issues are at the root of so many disruptions and contractions in the muscles and connective tissue in the first place. I will discuss issues around pain and boundaries throughout this book.

When I went to the Rolf Institute in 1983, my first instructor, Stacy Mills, led the class through a series of healing meditations. Whatever my expectations were of the Rolfing training, they certainly did not include that. I was surprised and delighted, and I felt confident that I was in the right place. Everything makes a full circle. Today, more than ever before, I feel how important it is to acknowledge the spiritual support I receive in my work. No matter how sophisticated the work is, it never supersedes the value of turning to a Power greater than myself, one that includes myself. When I am grounded spiritually, I avail myself of the most powerful techniques in my repertoire.

At the Body Therapy Center in Palo Alto, California, I teach a course entitled "Advanced Techniques in Body Therapy." The students in this course are graduates of the basic or advanced degree program at the Body Therapy Center, or professionals earning their living doing body therapy. Although I have been teaching this particular class since about 1983, I still feel just as happy before each class as I did in the beginning. As a student myself, I find it rewarding to work with these people, watching their effectiveness and their connections with clients sprout to new and exciting levels. In the process of learning techniques in body therapy, the participants invariably learn about their own bodies.

Recently, on the last night of an eight-week class, a woman was eager to share with the rest of the group that she had just developed an awareness of the feelings in her pelvis for, it seemed to her, the first time. Prior to the class, she felt that she had been out of touch with her body from below the waist. Needless to say, this was an important discovery. She had strong feelings and insights, and her behavior changed by virtue of the new information she had about her body. Her body moved more freely, and she felt able to contain a greater sexual charge. Although she released some old, buried emotions, there was essentially no upset, volatile, or cathartic reaction. For this lucky individual, the awareness brought with it happiness and pleasure. Although she had a greater understanding about some mysteries from her past, this event occurred primarily in present time. The woman was able to move forward with greater command and awareness of her body.

Sometimes people think that it is a lot of work to let go. But, once you learn how to do this, you may discover that in fact it is considerably more work to hang on. For this woman, it became more difficult to split herself off from her body than to live in and feel her body. As a facilitator in this process, I take pleasure in being near a person who freely moves toward greater expansiveness and lesser resistance. This is my fuel.

Teaching this class inspired me to devise the following list of values that I hold regarding body therapy and my work with clients. Understanding what is important to me enables me to stay more focused in my work. Each of the values I list will show up throughout this book in a variety of contexts.

VALUES

Support. An individual who holds his body rigidly often does not know how to let go. I can hold a person like this in such a way that he does not need to hold himself. Through the words I choose, the quality of my touch, and the way I use my own body, I consciously offer this support throughout the entire session. For the client, the release can happen on levels other than the most obvious (the physical). I can offer support for his emotions in such a way that he feels safe to release on the emotional level as well. If I hold my client just so, he may discover that it is superfluous to hold himself. I use various elements in the physical environment as a metaphor for support. This includes my body, the Rolfing table, gravity, the ground, pillows, chairs, and so on.

Presence. My clients must feel that I am there for them, in the room, in present time. Every time I go into my treatment room, I consciously release the distractions from my own life, the ones that would disrupt my mental concentration while I work. Some days it feels I must release something about the size of a Mack truck, but to the best of my ability, I bring myself into present time. This is the only way in which healing can occur. Also, if I am present, I have modeled how it is to leave a pile of distractions outside of the treatment room door. This is one of many examples of how the healing process involves my client's and my own presence equally.

Acceptance. A lack of self-acceptance can play a key role in preventing an individual from moving ahead in the therapeutic, or healing process. The client is often angry at his back, his neck, or *himself* for hurting. I am not saying that this anger is not allowed, or that it is bad. But the person stands a better chance of feeling better (getting healthier, hurting less, having more energy, and so on) if the so-called negative emotions from the past are resolved. As a therapist, I represent and therefore model this acceptance. I offer an alternative to self-recrimination.

Left brain/right brain coordination. I have learned academically and perceive intuitively that the two halves of the brain carry equal weight. At any moment while I work, either or both halves are operant and valued. Blending what I sense (intuition) with what I know (cognition) is the basis for my most effective work and decision making.

Involvement. My clients know that I am interested in who they are and that I am concerned about them. For years I trained extensively in ways of keeping an "appropriate professional distance" from my clients, but I have finally realized that it works for me to feel close to my clients and for them to feel close to me. It has been my experience that clients tend to get more involved in their own recovery and healing process when I am willing to go through it with them. When I offer information that would enable an individual to feel better in his body, including ways to release pain and other unwanted symptoms, the individual is more apt to accept this information if we have established a comfortable involvement with each other. Naturally, the level of intimacy varies, depending on the client's personality and on my process with the client.

My involvement with my clients also becomes a way for me to share parts of myself that may shed light on blocks or rough spots in their own health issues. This involvement, however, must never be a way for me to fulfill a longing or need of my own, one that is more appropriately met for me by a friend, a family member, or a helping professional. With this as a guideline, I am free to be open and reveal aspects of myself, perhaps for the edification of the client, perhaps as part of the bonding.

Love. If I can't love someone, I can't work with him. The work may be technically satisfactory, but the essential juice is missing. I owe my clients more than technical proficiency. Let's define love as having an open heart. I don't have to be in a state of spiritual rhapsody to feel love for my clients. But with my heart open, the possibility for a loving, healing connection is there. My work carries a stronger element of compassion—and compassion is the magic X factor in healing work.

Perseverance. People who have been suffering from pain feel great strength in knowing that a professional will go the full nine yards with them. Many times people want to give up on themselves, once again resigning themselves to the same pattern of pain or dysfunction to which they have become accustomed. Time is an enormous factor in the healing equation. Changing habits is often quite an ordeal for people, especially when they are fiercely attached, for whatever reason, to beliefs that helped perpetuate the problems in the first place. If my own skills fall short, my perseverance may take the form of helping a client find another professional who may have more answers than I do.

Nonattachment. The other side to the idea of perseverance is that I cannot be attached to any particular result or response on the part of the client. Many elements shape how a person unravels health and physical problems. As I do the best work I can do, I also must honor the inner self of the person with whom I am working. The client is in the process of learning many important things about himself. If I project my agenda or time line on his healing process, I may interrupt other equally vital lessons that are being learned. Most often when I catch myself rushing a client faster than his natural rhythm, it is for my own ego gratification, or because I have gotten impatient. In these cases, I am not ultimately supporting the client, and I need to change my demeanor, on his behalf. This can take the form of a dialogue with the client, a change in my technique, or physically backing off to give the client and myself a little breathing room.

Embodiment/empowerment. My most important job is to teach the people with whom I work how to live in their bodies more responsibly, consciously, and effectively. This includes working with a client to examine attitudes and beliefs about his body that may play a hidden role in perpetuating chronic health problems. It is significant for an individual to shift to a position in which he feels in charge of his body, and thus capable of making positive changes on his own.

I never met Dr. Rolf. She died a few years before I began my training. But yoga influenced her greatly as she began to formulate her work, and I believe I am carrying out her vision to its completion. I am motivated by a passion for my work and by the joy I receive in working with people as they open to new levels of self- and body awareness. At this stage in my development, I cannot imagine a more exciting or effective way to help people achieve such positive, powerful changes in their bodies, their relationships to the Earth, and, consequently, their lives. I deal with beings living in physical bodies, having experiences that are uniquely human. Whether I help them balance their meridians, their chakras, their triangle pose, or their connective tissue, I am dealing with the quality of life, with people's ability to cope effectively and get maximum pleasure out of being alive.

* * * * *

As I was putting the final touches on this book, I had a recurring concern regarding the context in which I wanted to present this material: the big picture, if you will. I never doubt the personal value I get from this work. In my own ever-changing world, my work has been a constant—perhaps constantly evolving, but also a constant source of enrichment and fulfillment for the past twenty-one years. Furthermore, I am fortunate and grateful to have many teachers, colleagues, clients, students, and friends who share, to varying degrees, my enthusiasm for studying bodies, health, and consciousness.

Nevertheless, this issue of context has persisted. I longed for a way to tell my story, to communicate the value that I find professionally and personally in being a Rolfer and a yoga and movement teacher, and to somehow voice an understanding that my world and my values have relevance to many people. How could I share my convictions, my passion, yet avoid seeming dogmatic? Because this material deals with, among other topics, learning to be open as part of our evolution, it is a vision of mine to deal with this information while remaining open myself. For me, that includes acknowledging other realities and points of view.

For years I have spoken about Rolfing and yoga as excellent vehicles for learning how to make life-supporting decisions. For a long time, this idea was the greatest context in which I could study and present my work. But I have recently come to a greater understanding of the fact that my relationship to the Earth is a fundamental element in the expression of my fullest potential as a human being. Once we understand that we are dealing with our relationships to the Earth, where we find inevitable support from the gravitational field, we can't help but discover spiritual dimensions of life that appear to be ever-widening and ever-deepening.

Simultaneous to my preparation of the final draft of this manuscript, my friend Oz Crosby handed me a copy of Vice President Al Gore's book *Earth in the Balance*. Oz said simply, "I think you should read this." Feeling moved many times while reading this extremely important book on the Earth and the environment, I realized what this context was, the one for which I had been searching.

I understand that my evolution is directly related to my connection to the Earth. I want to feel safe and in harmony with my environment. I want to be supported so I feel able to relax within the gravitational field, *to let the Earth hold me and nurture me*. To the extent that I can do this, my life will be that much more meaningful, both personally and interpersonally. *My willingness and ability to make life-supporting decisions have relevance in terms of my own evolution only to the degree that these decisions are earth-supporting decisions as well.* As we know, the Earth is changing rapidly. My own development is insignificant unless I give back to the Earth, helping to ensure the safety and security of this planet for myself, my children, the people with whom I live and work, and future generations. Although the challenge to live consciously, both in my body and on this Earth, may appear overwhelming, the benefits of rising to the occasion are inestimable.

Rosie Spiegel
San Carlos, California
December 1993

PREFACE

This book is designed to help bridge the gap between the world of body therapy and the world of hatha yoga. If you are already involved in either Rolfing or yoga, you may discover, reading the following chapters, that you have more in common with those who follow the other path than you imagined.

I offer this book to bodyworkers, yoga teachers, health practitioners, bodywork and movement instructors, and their clients and students. If I have done a good job, you will begin a love affair with yoga and your body similar to the one I have had for many years.

I will be using Rolfing as a frame of reference for describing the nuances and intricacies of effective, change-oriented bodywork. I have trained extensively in a variety of methodologies, and in this particular system I see the greatest potential for actual structural alterations. Rolfing is a sophisticated form of body therapy, designed to improve the human structure from a functional and mechanical point of view.

Dr. Ida P. Rolf, the grande dame of Rolfing, developed and taught her work from the 1960s up until her death in 1979. Years before her ideas gained popularity, she worked as a biochemist at the Rockefeller Foundation. Originally she devised Rolfing in response to a health problem that her son had, at a time when medical doctors were not helping. In the early days of her work, she was influenced by other professionals, including osteopaths and yoga instructors. Many schools and philosophies of body therapy find their origins in Rolfing, or Structural Integration, as it is also called.

Dr. Rolf is remembered as a scientist as well as a healer. The work she taught is hands-on. We do not rely on high-tech equipment to effect change in the body. Rolfing is a system that has its roots in natural healing. Part of all Rolfers' training is learning to see the body from both a structural and an energetic point of view. We use our minds as well as our intuition.

Dr. Rolf originally taught Rolfing as a ten-part series of hands-on manipulative treatments. In the basic Rolfing training, this series, or what we call the "recipe," prevails to this day. The training has evolved over the years to include movement work, emotional support, and various ways of developing self-exploration on the part of the client. Although the ten-session approach is an excellent working model, most advanced Rolfers, including myself, find that the work lends itself to creativity and spontaneity. Sometimes the recipe is expanded or modified to meet the unique needs of the client.

The Rolfer's focus is the fascia, or connective tissue, which is found throughout the entire body. The role of the fascia is to bind, support, and differentiate the internal organs, bones, blood vessels, and muscle tissue. To a large extent the fascia is responsible for the shapes of our bodies. All postural problems, including chronic pain and discomfort, ultimately have an impact on the connective tissue. We find that by releasing the holding in the connective tissue, the Rolfer can help the client experience a reduction of pain, improved posture and health, and an improvement in the way in which he experiences life in his unique body.

We work the connective tissue with our hands. Through a combination of direct pressure, stretching, energy techniques, and manipulations, the Rolfer reorganizes the fascial webbing throughout the body. The client's experience ranges from intense pleasure (because it feels so marvelous to get relief from chronic tension) to mild discomfort. I will talk more about this throughout the book, but for now I will say that it is my particular style to attempt to find ways that minimize or eliminate the client's pain during the Rolfing sessions.

Rolfers have different styles and different specialties. Many are experts in cranial-sacral therapy, for example, which requires a light touch. Fortunately, the work lends itself to considerable variations in personal style and creativity.

Because it is my goal to lengthen the parts of my client's body that have succumbed to tension and stress, I often stretch the various areas that have shortened. Having taught yoga for twelve years before becoming a Rolfer, I take advantage of my opportunity to blend two approaches, thereby enhancing the effectiveness of each. The yoga stretches that are part of the hatha branch of the eight-limbed system of Ashtanga Yoga are a natural complement to the Rolfing.

The physical and spiritual aspects of yoga blend naturally with healing work in general and with Rolfing in particular. Yoga often produces a release or a change that is seemingly impossible for the Rolfer to achieve with her hands only. One of the difficulties in Rolfing is that the Rolfer has to use considerable pressure in certain areas of the body where the client has stored tension. The amount of pressure needed to release the holding in the connective tissue is frequently more than the client can tolerate and therefore becomes counterproductive. A yoga stretch *designed to produce change in the same area of the body* is often perceived by the client as less invasive. Sometimes it is easier for the client to unfold and release from chronic holding while being stretched, rather than pressed. Yoga stretches make the Rolfer's work easier, more efficient, and more effective.

The reverse is also true. The Rolfer's hands can facilitate definite and positive change for the yoga student who has found himself stuck at a certain level of resistance. Sometimes just being touched exactly at the site of the holding can have a significant impact on the individual whose goal it is to release physically.

The Iyengar method is an extremely popular style of hatha yoga. B. K. S. Iyengar, who lives in Pune, India, has made a great contribution to the therapeutics of yoga by virtue of the precision and structural considerations that are inherent to his teaching style. I am trained in the Iyengar method, and I have visited Mr. Iyengar in India several times for teacher training courses. From the mid-1970s through the mid-1980s Iyengar yoga was my main focus. My training with Mr. Iyengar has been invaluable. Adding a structural perspective to my understanding of the asanas was one of the most significant influences in my work since I began in 1972.

Nevertheless, I am not an Iyengar teacher, and I do not think of my work now as following the Iyengar method. Frankly, I have moved away from the rigidity that often accompanies that teaching. After studying, practicing, and teaching the Iyengar method for more than ten years, I found in subsequent trainings and through my private practice that there was more to yoga than holding the asanas and doing the perfect pose. Currently my interest lies more in implementing the stretches as an educational process for myself and for the student. I learned this from doing bodywork for so many years. Ironically, I did not learn about the relevance of hatha yoga to living in our bodies through my yoga training. Instead, I learned this from my bodywork training, Rolfing in particular.

To a certain extent, the value of practicing yoga lies in the moment; the focus, the mental serenity, the strengthening, and the physical relaxation add up to a marvelous and worthy experience. I feel it is even more important, however, that the yoga student be given information that he can apply to his daily routine. For example, does a simple forward bend offer any insights into a more efficient way to tie your shoes? As you release the back of your head in a forward bend, what does this teach you about letting go of a particular way your neck hurts when you bend over to pick up something?

Doing the perfect yoga asana is relatively superficial compared to what my goals are. My commitment is to empower the yoga student to glean something from each and every moment of practicing the asanas that will translate into usable lessons of how to live more effectively, consciously, and happily in his physical body. This is particularly true for the time between the practice sessions. Have you ever wondered why we call it practice? What is it that we are practicing for?

The lessons that show up in life itself may have more long-lasting consequences and may be more pertinent than an insight, or realization, that occurs while doing the yoga. This is not to disparage a regular yoga practice in any way. On the contrary, I am a strong advocate of regular practice for my clients and my students. But I am an even stronger advocate of living consciously in our bodies at all times, not just during yoga class or while in the Rolfer's office.

* * * * *

There are two parts to this book. Part 1 deals with topics related to Rolfing and yoga from a variety of perspectives. These chapters, 1 through 11, are designed to paint a rich and colorful picture for you about Rolfing and yoga, in particular how they enhance each other when combined in a multidisciplinary approach. Whether you consider Rolfing and yoga as art, science, or therapy, your knowledge of the various aspects of each will enrich your involvement with them.

Part 2 contains instructions for following a yoga program that is complementary to the Rolfing series. The asanas are organized to match the objectives of the Rolfing sessions, hour by hour; the goal of each asana is the same as that of the matching Rolfing session. My main reason for blending the two is to provide an approach that is greater than the sum of its parts. Those of you who have already been Rolfed will find these asanas excellent for allowing you to perpetuate the positive changes that occurred during the time you were receiving the work. The asanas are an excellent home study course.

In my own practice, I find there are issues in my body that are best resolved through stretching, breathing, and working on my own. At other times, I feel a strong need to seek professional help. Sometimes a Rolfer's skilled hands can facilitate a release or help me become more aware in areas where I was unsuccessful in the privacy of my own practice. With time and practice, you learn how to meet the unique requirements of your own body, basically giving yourself what you need under a wide variety of circumstances. The most exciting part of all is that this is all quite learnable.

* * * * *

In writing this book, I struggled with the awkward dilemma of *he/she* pronouns. Finally I settled on referring to the professionals by using feminine pronouns and the clients and students by using masculine pronouns. Although this is an arbitrary classification, it at least helps clarify which person I am referring to. Please bear with me.

Part

ONE

1

Chapter ONE

Rolfing and Yoga:
Blending Two Disciplines

One of the great joys of being a Rolfer and teaching yoga and movement is witnessing the metamorphosis of the individuals and groups with whom I have the privilege of working. For the person new to Rolfing and yoga, a whole new world of personal change and self-development opens. The types of changes an individual goes through when he gets Rolfed and when he does yoga are frequently quite different from responses he has had to any prior experience. Letting go of tension and becoming more supple are examples of these changes. These are acquired skills, ones that improve with practice. Many people who take part in these types of therapies have had no prior experience in any activity oriented toward increasing body awareness and becoming more relaxed. Fortunately, previous experience is not a prerequisite for achieving positive results from being Rolfed or doing yoga. The body learns to expand and to become more flexible. But as in all acquired skills, time and practice are two vital factors in mastering these abilities.

Learning to relax and to let go comes easier to some people than others, and this ability depends on many factors. Some bodies seem to be less pliant than others. Some individuals have personal histories that have left their bodies with more torques, twists, and restrictions. A serious accident or disease would affect the general structural condition of a body, intensifying the inherent challenge of being Rolfed or doing yoga. It is the goal of the Rolfer and yoga teacher to help soften the adhesions and restrictions in the muscles, and connective tissue, and certain physical conditions, such as the two just mentioned, make this job more difficult. Sedentary or elderly people may find that their bodies have stiffened from lack of use. And although many athletes have kept their bodies supple and aligned, the bodies of others are ravaged with abuse from years of intensive, demanding sports.

Events in the psychological history of an individual may also prevent him from letting go easily and naturally. Most forms of physical, sexual, or emotional abuse leave the body and the psyche wounded on some level.

These wounds become material for the client and the Rolfer or yoga instructor to work on together. For example, adults who were abused as children often tell a story in their bodies about the emotional climate in which they lived when they were quite young. Many may still be armored by the protective coating so pervasive in their musculatures. As small, unprotected people, they adapted to their environment—at an enormous cost to their physical integrity. They made their bodies rigid to ensure their survival. As adults, they are habituated to these holding patterns. The environment may not be an actual threat to these grown-ups, as it was when they were little. But the long-term holding in their musculatures prevents these adults from perceiving their world as safe. If they continue to guard their bodies, the world will continue to appear threatening. These adults require rigorous retraining to learn to effectively release the physical holding that stems from experiences in the past. Yoga and Rolfing are excellent arenas in which to process this material, but the work can be very challenging indeed.

Some people who have never known anything different actually think they were born with bodies that are stiff and uncomfortable and that do not move. But although genetics certainly factor in, the individual's personal history must also be considered. I have seen many individuals make assumptions about their bodies that deny painful facts about their past. For example, I recently heard a student comment that she was "born with" tight hamstrings. She lacked an understanding about how her body had learned to adapt as she moved through life. "Blaming" her tight hamstrings on a "birth defect" was an effective way to avoid looking honestly at what her body was expressing in present time or at what her body had brought forward from the past. As this particular woman progresses in her Rolfing, the changes will not only be physical, insofar as her body becoming more supple and relaxed. She will inevitably learn more about herself, and the reasons behind all of the holding

5

may reveal themselves. This information will aid her in moving ahead to make more positive and personal changes. For instance, she may notice her relationships with her immediate family shifting to one where there is more honesty and more love. This would be a direct result of her having learned to release the guard that had been in her physical body, but that had affected her on other levels as well.

Many variables affect our ability to move through the blocks in our physical bodies. Ultimately, becoming more aware of and more sensitive to the data from your personal past is something you do in order to release tension and to increase your general flexibility in present time. Gaining an inner sense of the possible meaning behind the rigidities in your musculature really helps. The data can be something relatively uncomplicated, such as a realization that you have worked competitively in your body with little regard for your own limitations. Living in your body with this kind of attitude would produce specific limitations in your general flexibility and overall tension level. Once you become aware of this, you can make changes accordingly. I had a client once who was so addicted to his performance as a runner, he refused to take a break even when his body was in intense pain due to various injuries. He told me that he never rested for recuperation; I told him that he would need to examine this aspect of his lifestyle in order for our work together to be successful. The changes were made, reluctantly at first. Eventually, he was very happy with the positive changes in his body. I was even more pleased with the changes in his attitude.

Accepting whatever limitations you begin with makes it easier to accomplish positive change. Making peace with the past is often the prerequisite to learning the necessary lessons to make a change in the present. Have the courage to move through these blocks, even if the movement is slow-going, hard work, intense, or unpleasant at times. Recently a woman in her fifties told me that she believed she had never relaxed in her entire life. The idea of letting go of her carefully guarded armor scared her. I agreed with her that yes, relaxing can be quite scary. And then I encouraged her to let go anyway; she would probably grow to like the results of finally allowing her body to relax.

Many people rush through anything resembling personal growth, anxious and eager for quick results. Relaxing through this process and giving yourself time play major parts in your becoming healthier and more conscious in your body. The frustration many people feel while working to change their bodies is often the result of having imposed unrealistic expectations on themselves in an unreasonable time frame. This in itself is a behavioral pattern. In both Rolfing and yoga, you can learn to work with time.

It is imperative that you work with someone who has patience with your progress. I have been with yoga teachers and body therapists (as a student and as a client) who seemed to have an agenda that I should progress to a certain point while under their tutelage. Their egos were somehow on the line, and it was my job to make them look good. Imposing expectations in this way is inappropriate and unprofessional. If I find myself projecting that kind of energy to my client, I catch myself quickly, back off (literally move away), take some deep breaths, reorganize my thoughts, and then gradually move back into the person's energy field. I monitor my own demeanor, having remembered what the contract is. When I am working in a healing capacity, it is my job to honor and support an individual's inner time frame. (This does not preclude my being encouraging and at times assertive with my clients and students. I must not, however, step outside of the role of facilitator by projecting my expectations upon a person, who has his own abilities and limitations. These factors are an important part of his process.)

You can't force or hurry the wonderful results of Rolfing or yoga. It is an oxymoron to speak of relaxing faster and harder. Ultimately, the facilitator

7

and client work together to set the pace of the work in progress. The facilitator may read cues from the client in order to determine how to move and at what speed. The work is a dance between client or student and therapist or instructor, in which the professional closely tracks the sensitivity, receptivity, and readiness of the recipient.

Certain individuals follow a pattern of either procrastinating or rushing, in an attempt to open to new levels of physical and emotional release. Finding a balance then becomes key. The professional becomes responsible for teaching the client or student how to love himself and be patient with himself as he integrates this new and challenging information into his mind and body, at whatever pace—especially when it is hard work. The client may perceive the hard work as being stressful, a situation that is likely to set in motion his patterns.

Deane Juhan, in *Job's Body*, has an informative point of view on this kind of teaching and learning:

> Then bodywork is essentially *education*. As it is in the case of most forms of education, it is important that it be pleasurable. The mind tends to recoil from pain and ignore unpleasantness when it can, and for this reason we usually retain facts better when they come to us associated with feelings of pleasure. Pleasure engages our relaxed attentiveness. And besides, the possibilities of the body as a source of pleasure are precisely what we normally forget when we are ill or injured or deeply confused. This does not mean that the titillating of the nerve ends is the *point* of bodywork...Clear sensory information is the *content* of effective bodywork; pleasure is simply the medium which is most apt to help us focus upon those contents.[1]

This then becomes an excellent argument for the value of keeping Rolfing and yoga at a level below intolerable pain. I qualify the word *pain* with *intolerable* because certain kinds of pain are agreeable to the Rolfing client or to the student of yoga. We say, "It hurts good." If the discomfort addresses an area of old holding in your body, the psychological and physical relief associated with *releasing* the pain often overshadows the pain itself. This is comparable to a good cry. If your body longs to release its chronic restrictions, you do not necessarily want to avoid some experience of discomfort. I believe that I do not hurt my clients. I do, however, touch their bodies where they already hurt.

While a person is in a positive frame of mind, certain chemicals released by the brain, such as endorphins, actually facilitate learning. The pleasurableness of this mental state makes the learning process agreeable and helps the individual to internalize the learned material. My father used to tell me that prior to a major exam in college, once he had completed his studying, he used to go to the movies. For him, relaxing before the exam got him better grades than cramming did. He was telling me, in his own words, that relaxing his mind was a learning tool he had discovered and used naturally.

On the other hand, pressure, or duress, prevents the student from receiving, understanding, and internalizing the material being presented. Tension and resistance inhibit learning. If a person beats himself up for not performing better, for not letting go faster, for not relaxing better, this internal conflict of interest will actually thwart his work. The conflict is between one internalized self longing to release the blocks and to move toward greater freedom and another internalized self having recriminating thoughts and feelings that energetically and even biochemically depress any innate ability to let go, to learn, and to make positive change.

In many instances, only physical objectives prompt an individual to pursue Rolfing or yoga. Yet frequently, as the sessions progress, it becomes obvious that there is an emotional or spiritual root to the physical tensions and problems. Ironically, the negativity and self-deprecation that appear in the character of a person being Rolfed or doing yoga are related to some of the

9

issues that prompted that person to do the work in the first place. Even if he has not found it necessary to pursue therapy because of his tendencies to make himself wrong or to judge his performance critically, these tendencies may show up as holding (as in holding back, or holding on) to some rigidity in the body's structure. Conversely, positive, loving, flowing attitudes of the self are often reflected in a perceptible suppleness in the soft tissue and musculature. Self-love is the root of many types of healing.

There are even classic representations in the body of such nonphysical problems as chronic fear or a compulsive need to be in control. Frequently fear will show up in the body as a pair of shoulders pulled upward toward the ears. As long as the shoulders are "frozen," the individual has a less likely chance of enjoying his life free from debilitating fear. People governed by a compulsion to remain in control often suck in their abdomens, contract their anal sphincter muscles, and suppress their breathing. For individuals with chronic fear or with issues regarding control, focusing on the body, actually releasing tension during times when certain issues are being provoked, is an elegant way to treat psychological disturbances while grounding these disturbances in physical reality. In this way, body awareness and body therapy can pick up where "talk therapy" leaves off.

Sue had many years of psychotherapy. Despite all the work, she seemed unable to effectively handle a chronic fear and a nagging anxiety regarding money and security. One evening, during the time she was getting Rolfed and doing yoga regularly, her husband "pushed her buttons" regarding security and money by announcing that the couple had no money to pay the mortgage that month. Sue's body went into near convulsions: it tightened intensively around her solar plexus, her breathing became spasmodic, and her body seemed to completely shut down. With the awareness that she had in her body, Sue closely examined in detail the amazing process she was undergoing. She was having a powerful experience and was witnessing herself—staying mindful—while doing so. What came out of this event was a full understanding of precisely *what she did and how she did it* when her anxieties about security overpowered her body.

Later, Sue described to me with incredible exactness how she had managed to get her body into such an uncomfortable position that evening. She said, "It was just incredible! I pulled tight around my entire belly. It was as if I could feel myself sending these chemicals from my brain that were full of anxiety-provoking agents. I felt myself put lots of pressure in my legs, and I could feel how I drew my breath in tightly. I tightened my muscles so much that I was trembling. While these powerful things were happening, I heard a small but definite voice in my head say, 'Okay, this is how you do this. You have the tiger by the tail. You can undo this pain you are in.' I felt myself begin to back out of these holding patterns, and move in the opposite direction. It was very gradual and it took about sixty minutes. It was amazing and incredibly valuable. I released the fear and the intense anxiety, and I opened my breath. I did it on purpose! It was a remarkable experience."

Sue often said that the psychotherapy she had been through had been extremely valuable, but that talking about her anxiety went only so far. It was the *direct experience of anxiety and fear*, what her body did when these feelings became overpowering in the moment, that finally enabled her to make a change in her behavior and release an old, chronic, debilitating fear. Clearly it was the blend of the influences of psychotherapy and body therapy that finally catapulted Sue into a new level of responsibility, awareness, and positive change.

Since that time, Sue has told me that her body now stays much calmer and more open when her old buttons get pushed. She can choose to avoid going down that particular well-trodden path of a familiar group of responses. Having learned what she did, she gradually was able to consciously deactivate her whole anxiety reaction. And as she released some old perceptions that were disabling for her, her body became able to experience her environment in a new way. Sue felt strongly that her body was now ready to process much of the information she had been gathering for some time. Subsequently, when issues of security and money arose, Sue was not inhibited by her fear and anxiety. Thus she became more competent and creative in solving her own problems.

This example illustrates the power of continually exposing ourselves to the kind of somatic data that encourage us to move toward positive change. Even for myself, certain "breakthroughs" haven't happened until after what has seemed like a long period of putting energy into letting go of old perceptions and limiting beliefs. Despite our modern society's sophisticated psychological understanding, the body often appears to have a "mind of its own." We need to give ourselves time, to be patient with ourselves. This is a key factor in the healing equation.

Gradually, with patience, over time, your body is stretched, loosened, softened, and lengthened. (See table 1.1.)

Table 1.1: Effect of Stretching and Manipulation on Soft Tissue

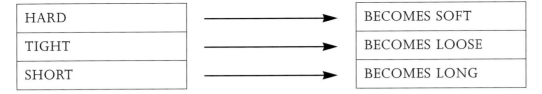

HARD	→	BECOMES SOFT
TIGHT	→	BECOMES LOOSE
SHORT	→	BECOMES LONG

Through Rolfing and yoga, the self emerges in a state of heightened awareness of the body. (See figure 1.1.) A friend of mine, Leslie, is a yoga instructor and massage therapist who is particularly well acquainted with her body. She talks about anything that happens to her in terms of how it feels in her body. If she has gone to the coast for the weekend and had a wonderful time, she might say how fluid her breath felt the whole time she was there. If she has dealt with a difficult passage in her life, such as a break-up with a sweetheart, she will inform me of the heaviness she feels in her chest and how her legs seem unwilling to get her to the next place where she needs to be.

Figure 1.1: Through Rolfing and yoga, the self emerges in a state of heightened awareness and physical embodiment.

We are made up of energy in the form of matter. If our bodies are dense, tense, and inflexible, we experience our lives from the viewpoint of someone limited in his expression and movement. Even biochemically, as the tissue softens in response to the pressure and stretching associated with Rolfing and yoga, the musculature relaxes and our physiology changes. We feel in our bodies an openness and expressiveness, and our perspective changes dramatically.

Working to change the way our bodies handle and express energy can have far-reaching effects. The story of Leah illustrates this. Leah found herself constantly drawn to men who were chronic underachievers, were rather dull, and lacked movement and motivation. In a way, this was a case of like seeking like: Leah had similar problems with her own chronic low energy. At this stage in her development, she would have been unable to tolerate the company of a high-energy, creative, exuberant man. She was easily overwhelmed by high-energy people. Her own lethargy was pervasive.

Shortly after Leah began her Rolfing treatments, she joined a yoga class. During a six-month period, she learned to release the chronic restrictions on her breathing and found herself sighing deeply many times during the day. She grew to crave the intense rush of oxygen as it moved into her reawakening musculature. Her back pain of twenty years gradually became a thing of the past. Symbolically, she was learning not to hold herself back.

Leah's body was waking up and she knew it. She reported to me that on one occasion, while taking the same walk to her workplace that she had taken countless times before, she couldn't help but skip merrily down the street, a behavior that was somewhat shocking even to herself. Leah said the urge to move had overwhelmed her; she had felt she simply had to succumb to these surges of energy in her body. Gradually, over the next year, Leah began to attract and be attracted to men and women with greater vitality and higher levels of energy. These people had, in general, a much better self-image than her friends of the past.

This change can be explained by Leah's getting her own energy moving. Her body went from being relatively inert to moving, pulsating, actually throbbing with life. Leah needed more stimulation in order to feed her spirit, as she became accustomed to living life to its fullest.

Stories like the ones I tell here are not uncommon. People can change, and they do. Long-term benefits from the kinds of changes we are discussing are a function of an individual's ability to keep the work going. It would be easy if a few sessions of yoga or Rolfing changed a person once and for all. Realistically, however, involvement over time is the powerful agent for change. New lifestyle habits need considerable support, reassurance, and reinforcement to become ingrained. Often tension patterns and core issues need to be dealt with through a program of regular maintenance and tuning. When a person forgets what he has learned, a competent professional can help provide the necessary reminder. This process is identical in body-oriented therapy and in yoga, as well as in psychotherapy.

15

2

Chapter **TWO**

Learning Through Pain

Many people in our culture have learned to avoid pain and discomfort. The plethora of pain medication and muscle relaxants that many members of our society use attests to this. Each of us deals with pain and discomfort in a way that is based on a combination of learned and innate behavior. It may seem natural to withdraw from pain, even though this is not the only alternative.

Practitioners of yoga can learn to fully experience pain without contracting their bodies or their minds. For some kinds of pain, a nonmedical, nonpharmaceutical, natural approach, such as yoga, may be considerably more effective in helping the sufferer to learn to release the pain. This is especially true because much of what we call pain is a by-product of the body contracting in the first place. A stomachache is a perfect example.

When in pain, many people turn to a physician, whose advice is frequently regarded as gospel. This powerful source of support and authority frequently undermines the individual's natural healing abilities. A medicine that covers up pain often does virtually nothing to solve the problem at its source. For example, a drug designed to eliminate abdominal pain in an ulcer patient may relieve the individual's symptoms, but it will not help the patient learn to manage stress, relax, and release tension, thereby helping him to gain control of the overload of acids secreted by the stomach in response to tension, fear, and anxiety. Rolfing and yoga both encourage us to assume a much greater responsibility for and control over our health in general, and the relief of pain in our bodies in particular.

A remarkable event occurred in a workshop I was conducting recently in Portland, Oregon. The workshop was entitled "Yoga and Rolf Movement." The participants were yoga instructors, bodyworkers, and their clients. One participant, a woman named Jackie, had been brought by her yoga teacher, who had been frustrated by Jackie's physical problems.

Jackie walked with a distinct limp. While we were doing the movement work, I asked her about her body and why she walked as she did. She said that her limp was the result of a severe injury to her right ankle fifteen years ago. She told the group that, in spite of her pronounced limp, her foot did not bother her. Other parts of her body troubled her considerably, but she felt no pain in her foot.

I suggested to Jackie that she walk around the room, putting her weight on both feet and observing her right foot. Jackie first said that she couldn't possibly walk on her right foot; she knew that putting weight on that foot would be terribly painful. With my encouragement, however, she agreed to explore the feelings in what she called her bad foot.

When Jackie first put her weight on her right foot, she discovered that indeed there was pain. But she agreed to continue walking on that foot, gradually increasing her weight on that underused part of her body. In essence, I was asking her to reown her foot, to take it back. The pain subsided within a couple of minutes. That was exciting for her, for me, and for the rest of the group. But even more miraculously, Jackie began unwinding the chronic aches and pains that had developed in response to the need she had perceived fifteen years ago to favor that right foot. Her hip released a terrible pain. Her walk stabilized. Within moments, Jackie was feeling energy in and support from her body that she hadn't felt in years. I was able to be with Jackie for three days, during which time her foot remained free of pain.

19

THE PHYSICIAN'S ROLE

Many of my clients and students receive treatment from physicians simultaneous with being Rolfed and doing yoga. I have come to recognize a syndrome among some of these individuals, and I can spot it quickly. They have a deferential attitude toward physicians in all areas of health—in fact, in anything relating in any way to their bodies. I am not opposed to doctors. I work with physicians who refer their patients to me, and I take my children to a wonderful pediatrician. I do oppose the kind of doctor-patient relationship that fosters dependence upon the doctor, however, and that ultimately keeps the patient from exploring other possible routes to good health. It breaks my heart to see patients suffer because they are afraid to go outside of the traditional medical model. It takes only a modicum of intelligence to see that doctors don't have all of the answers.

That a physician is omniscient in the area of health and well-being is a fallacy perpetuated by certain patients and by doctors themselves. It is incredible to see grown, educated, otherwise responsible individuals give up their power when dealing with doctors. I have known people to seek *permission* from their physicians to do something regarding their own health or bodies (switching to a macrobiotic diet or getting Rolfed, for example)—even when the physicians knew absolutely nothing about these subjects! This reverence can, in the final analysis, steer the patient even further from the *state of optimal health, which is the state in which the patient is ultimately in charge of and responsible for his own body.*

The ideal role for the physician to take, *especially when dealing with a patient who has not learned to be wise about his own body,* is that of educator, coach, and mentor. The more a patient is informed about his own body, the more likely he will develop an intuitive sense that will ultimately guides him to make life-supporting decisions. The nuances and complexities of the doctor-patient relationship go beyond a dependence born of the patient's reluctance to assume responsibility for his own health. Empowerment, especially when it comes from a health provider, becomes a critical factor, allowing a patient to make substantial positive changes in his own health profile.

* * * * *

In the realm of "alternative" approaches to health and wellness, a number of highly effective techniques are used to conquer a wide variety of ills, including pain. In the introduction to this book I proposed that Rolfing and yoga could be so highly effective as to help you make modifications in your lifestyle. Turning to yourself as the authority for your own health, rather than looking elsewhere to validate your experience or have someone else take control of your body, is an excellent example of this shift in focus and responsibility. Following is a discussion of several natural, proven methods that you can implement to improve your health.

BREATH CONTROL

By concentrating on the sensations in your body, you learn to breathe fully when you notice that you are feeling tense, tight, or sore. The breath acts like a gentle massage, allowing your body to open from the inside. During a full inhalation, the pressure increases around the thorax, throat, abdomen, shoulders, chest, lower back, and sides of your torso. This increase in pressure can actually stretch and move tension out of the musculature. Expanding the vital capacity (a measure of the lung's potential for the greatest amount of air) is introduced in the first Rolfing hour, when the diaphragm is loosened. Dr. Rolf figured that, in order to sustain the tremendous release of energy in the subsequent Rolfing hours, the client must learn to take a full breath in the first lesson. In yoga, the focus on breathing provides for the intensity of the asanas and promotes relaxation. All yoga lessons include breathing instructions.

Many people tend to tighten their bodies and to hold their breath under a variety of stress-related experiences—pain, for example. Correcting this habit can be easy: Time, practice, and quality of instruction can make a real difference. After a short time, it is easy to see and feel that tightening around the breath may effectively deaden the feeling of pain, but does not correct the problem. In fact, this habit creates more problems by forcing the body into a compensatory response. In terms of compensating, there is often a negative net effect. By tightening around the pain, Jackie, the woman with the limp, had created a problem that was bigger than the one she was trying to solve. Her entire right leg and hip hurt and malfunctioned, not just the ankle. Expanding the body and breathing fully release the pain and the underlying tension that caused the pain.

In Jackie's case, she had been favoring the ankle that had been injured. The leg and hip on the same side as the hurt foot compensated for the initial injury by taking over the load that would be distributed to the foot in a well-integrated body. Compensations are like Band-Aids: Jackie was putting one holding pattern over the other. The result invariably complicates the initial problem.

I have worked with many asthmatics over the years. For many, the condition has a stress-related root. Frequently clients have been able to control their symptoms somewhat by relaxing and expanding around their breathing. In these cases, little or no drug intervention is necessary. These results do not occur overnight. Over weeks, months, or longer, the clients gradually and slowly release the tension in their bodies, which enables them to focus on a fuller, more complete breath. If strong emotions such as fear trigger attacks, these individuals realize they can help tame the symptoms by breathing comfortably, fully, and with undivided focus in the face of these emotions. Often psychotherapeutic intervention is an appropriate adjunct to body therapy in cases where strong emotional blocks play a role in the asthma. Sophisticated techniques using breath release can also provide miraculous physical and psychological results.

Once the patient is free of symptoms, remaining relaxed during stress or conflict is imperative. A recovering asthma sufferer may need to pay attention to the calming effects of his breath over his entire lifetime. I have known people who were asymptomatic for decades, only to have a flare-up during a period of intense emotional stress. The breathing difficulties came on suddenly, often before the person had the time to breathe and relax. One of the most lovely aspects of breath work, as it is taught through body therapy and yoga, is the idea that we can breathe fully all of the time. Breathing fully when we are calm, when we are not being provoked, is practice for the times we need to breathe fully in order to survive.

Medication is an external device used to control the symptoms and discomfort of asthma. For some people, asthma does have a purely medical or environmental root. But for others, it is a response to stress, tension, emotional trauma, or a suppressed respiratory system, the last of which results from one of the first three elements. For these people, the medical model is somewhat limiting in its view of asthma as simply a lung condition.

Recovery from asthma is an example of the dramatic effects of breath control. On a more mundane level, you can learn to relax with a deeper, more regular, more even breath even during times of stress. Rolfing and yoga address these issues directly. Learning these new skills can help you to take more control not only of your breath, but of your life.

2
3

DELIBERATE MOVEMENT

Deliberate movement includes expanding (rather than contracting) in response to pain. It also includes stretching your body out of the variety of holding patterns that tend to be by-products of modern living. Perhaps the intensity of Rolfing and yoga actually help teach you to "go with it"—"it" being the so-called negative feedback that we get from our bodies in the form of tension, pain, and limited range of motion. As an example, stiffness in the back usually indicates some sort of tightness and shortness in the musculature. In such a case, the back needs to lengthen. Tightening it to prevent the discomfort does nothing but reinforce the problem.

Frequently among my clientele and students I meet people who have learned *not to move*. These lessons have often come from well-intentioned but misinformed health professionals not trained in functional movement for rehabilitation. Even physicians who otherwise perform excellent medical services occasionally disable a patient who suffers minor structural injuries. For example, the neck brace is advisable for some cases of trauma to the cervical vertebrae. For the majority of stiff necks, some mild whiplash, and cervical pain, however, the body needs to move as part of the recovery. Proper, well-balanced movement itself is the vehicle that allows the pain to be released.

An immobilized neck, as well as the surrounding and supporting musculature, runs the risk of stiffening. Also, when the injured part of your body is immobilized, the rest of your body is forced to compensate and to move with severe limitations. If energy is blocked in the musculature, a limited range of motion and stiffening of the muscle and connective tissue will appear elsewhere in your body. It is extremely common, for example, for a neck injury to mysteriously manifest itself as pain in the lower back a few months after the original injury. This is the nature of compensation. Living with a limb, a muscle group, or a body part out of balance inevitably puts strain on other body parts. It becomes the work of your body to carry the load at some distance from the injury. Something leans to the right, and then something leans to the left to counter the effect of the imbalance. Learning to reown the parts of your body that have been knocked out of balance is a powerful therapeutic strategy.

I have given thousands of treatments for neck injuries in my twenty-plus years of practice. Invariably, results are best when I not only work the injured area with my hands, but also work closely with the client to determine the stretches and movement patterns that will give the neck the support it needs and offset further complications or damage. Frequently these stretches and movement work address areas of the body other than the injured area itself. If you imagine that the muscles are being governed by an energetic current moving through your body, then you understand that you need to address any disruption to that flow in order to correct any structural problem.

Frequent neck injuries may actually be related to structural problems elsewhere in the spine. This is another example of compensation: The body is attempting to counterbalance something that is out of alignment. Tension, fatigue, or pain may appear in the neck itself as a result of imbalances below the neck, because structural support is lacking in the areas below the neck. Immobilizing the neck would ameliorate the problem on a temporary basis, but would do nothing for the chronic nature or cause of the problem.

For example, if you had fallen prey to minor back stiffness ten years ago, you might have learned to protect yourself and to avoid the pain by holding your back rigid, as if it shouldn't or couldn't move. Your doctor might have told you, "Go to bed and lie flat on your back for two weeks. Don't move." You might now be experiencing complications in your hips and shoulders related to your compensations for the way in which you learned to hold your back. This scenario is an argument for moving the body intelligently, particularly in response to discomfort, rather than keeping it stiff.

Joanne recently discovered through Rolfing that as a small child, she had survived by keeping very still. She did not move. Because of the volatile behavior among her family members, including two alcoholic parents, Joanne had learned early on that she was more protected from the physical and emotional violence that dominated her home environment if she was not seen or heard. Through Rolfing, Joanne learned to move, particularly in response to triggers that brought old fears to the surface. She was able to recognize her tendency of clamping down. Consequently, she allowed herself to explore a new set of responses, namely keeping her body energies flowing through movement, particularly while under duress. Joanne continued breathing and actually focused on the feelings associated with her breathing when she recognized a potential threat in her environment. Walking and swinging her hips, arms, and shoulders were also part of the recipe that enabled Joanne to keep from internalizing the stress and tension in her own body. Through learning to breathe and move in this way, Joanne came to enjoy a body pain-free for the first time that she could remember. Her legs tracked evenly as she learned to release the squeezing in her pelvis. Her back and shoulders softened, which brought Joanne significant relief.

A couple of weeks before Joanne finished her Rolfing, she went to Los Angeles to attend her sister's wedding. Her parents, who she had not seen for several years, were there, as were her eight siblings. I saw Joanne right after she had returned from LA. She told me what an amazing experience it had been to watch her body's impulses to freeze. This urge had been considerably stronger while she was around her family, at her sister's wedding. After all, Joanne had learned this particular defensive coping strategy in her family. Because of her work with her body through Rolfing, however, she was able to release each of her many impulses. It required a monumental effort on her part to stay open while around her parents. Given how provocative the wedding must have been for Joanne, and given how new these skills and abilities were for her, I believe she did a commendable job integrating the new material into her life. She said her shoulders hurt a tiny bit on the flight coming home. After having had such a direct experience of the way she used to hold her body, she could understand why she used to hurt all the time.

In my practice, I frequently meet individuals whose bodies don't move because someone along the way has taught them not to move. This type of patterning begins as a way to protect the body or to defend oneself against psychological threats. Indeed, some holding patterns stem back to veritable survival issues. A child being molested cannot scream because of the danger posed by the perpetrator. His throat may remain contracted for forty years or more as he constantly guards against the terror locked inside. In many cases, these issues never get resolved. On a physical level, the same kind of thing occurs when someone believes that he will correct pain or discomfort by favoring the body part in question. As we have seen, this never works in the long term and is at best a temporary palliative. If your back hurts, holding your back tight or "tucking your tailbone under" replaces one tension pattern with another.

Let's examine this. Sometimes it is a myth that leads a person to protect his back. Wearing a girdle to strengthen the back is a classic example. If the girdle restricts movement, it may be simultaneously solving one problem and creating another. Most types of back pain would benefit from a soft, relaxed tummy—not one that is weak and flaccid, but one that is relaxed. Muscle tone is important, but that's different from contraction and rigidity. If your belly is strong and relaxed, than the strength is stored as potential, rather than as chronic tension that might exacerbate a problem with your back. Pain is a symptom that results from imbalance, strain, and random groups of tight and taut muscles. Deep relaxation, the opposite of "holding the tummy in" can do wonders for correcting long-term problems and pains. Holding the shoulders back to "open the chest" may have a slight merit cosmetically. But in truth, it carries a high price in terms of complications of an existing problem and loss of integrity to the structural alignment and balance of the entire shoulder girdle. The tension and effort required to hold the chest open defy any benefit to making this type of "correction" in the body.

A professional who is supposed to help a patient work through chronic physical pain or mend a recent, more acute structural or muscular injury needs to understand structure in order to give reliable advice. Unfortunately, people sometimes take their bodies to professionals who do not understand structure and who occasionally give advice that is not appropriate. Often the professional who is consulted regarding back problems or neck problems (or something related) does not know how to educate the client to move in order to handle and release the tightness or the pain. She instructs the client not to move. "Don't move" then becomes a euphemism for "I don't know how you should move, so let's play it safe and have you not move at all." This is surprisingly common, and often projects fear in the client's body. For some back problems, such as a ruptured vertebral disc, restricted movement may be the appropriate course. But it is extremely difficult for the client to know where to draw the line regarding movement. Therapeutic movement to treat an injury should be precise, especially when it is necessary to avoid contraindications. These precise lessons are taught by a professional who understands function and structure. Typically, the client would not stumble upon these corrections with little or no education.

Back and neck injuries are often acute and the result of a crisis. A yoga student of mine was recently vacationing in New York. A moving car jumped the curb and caught the woman between the front bumper of the car and a fence. She was terrified, naturally. But she immediately resorted to the breathing techniques she had learned in yoga. Against the advice of all the people who gathered at the accident, she began making micromovements in order to gradually be able to stretch out her legs and feet. She knew how to play the edges. In yoga, you learn to move without placing any stress on your body. Even at the hospital, the nurses and doctors seemed frightened by someone who wanted to keep her body relaxed after an accident. But this woman knew how to take care of her own body, despite the sharp warnings of helping professionals around her. A person less sophisticated about his body, without much wisdom of his own, would be more apt to freeze his body, further complicating the original injury.

This discussion is not meant to debunk all traditional medical precautions and first aid. Rather, it is designed to shed some light on what may be some glaring limitations of health care. In my value system, a natural, self-correcting healing is by far the best method, whenever possible. The more a person gets involved in finding his own wellness, the more the natural wisdom of his own body is reinforced. Working with a competent professional can set the stage for the flowering of a successful relationship between the patient and his own body.

VISUALIZATION

The attitude of the patient is a critical factor in the healing equation. For a patient to have all the information pertinent to his condition on a psychological level requires a sensitivity with which few people are born but which most can learn. An intimate relationship with your psyche—one in which you know what role your thoughts, feelings, and beliefs play in your overall health profile—is achievable. Some physicians work with their patients using this holistic approach. Bernie Siegel uses visualization along with other nonmedical methods successfully with cancer patients at Yale Medical Center.

In order to cure disease and the physical side effects of tension, stress, and anxiety, I have discovered it is essential for the patient to get clear on a mental and feeling level, that is, rid himself of any ambivalence about becoming completely well and free of symptoms. This may seem obvious at first. But people can learn to attach themselves to pain or discomfort in ways that are creative and far below the conscious mind. This is not to say that a person's disease is "all in his head," nor is it a covert way of blaming the patient for his problems. Whenever there is pain, disease, or disability, the opportunity to learn from the experience, in terms of sharpening one's acuity and perspicacity about inner process, is always present. It is important to be open to personal work at this level. Often health issues resolve themselves when an individual reveals to himself conflicting thoughts or ulterior motives that lie at the root of his physical problems. This work needs to be done with a competent therapist.

Recently I gained a delightful understanding about my own ability to choose wellness, which is, in a way, what we are discussing here. I felt that a head cold was flirting with me, luring me toward a bout with a stuffy nose, sinus congestion, and a general bad feeling. I saw the sickness as a train and called it the Sickness Train. There it was, beckoning me. I chose not to get on the train, and it took off down the track, leaving me behind with my clear nose and breathing. I have offered this imagery to my clients, who have reported positive results when they used it.

PATIENT BEWARE!

3
1

When I met Jack, he had his chin pressed with considerable force down toward his chest. It was as if there were contact cement between the tip of his chin and his throat. Twenty-five years before a physician had told him that a coughing fit had caused him to "throw his neck out" and had dislodged his brain stem. Even though this ridiculous diagnosis was subsequently dismissed by another physician, it was enough to scare Jack, who had since heeded the first doctor's advice not to move or lift his head at all. Taking the physician literally, Jack had not moved his neck or head for all those years. Simple activities, such as driving, eating, and sleeping, were incredibly difficult for Jack.

In terms of our work together, it required quite a bit of time and focus to pry his chin from his neck. The compensations in his body were a series of rigid holding patterns in the connective tissue. To look up, Jack had to throw his hips forward considerably in order to counterbalance the maneuver of his entire torso backward. As he lifted from his navel, he scrunched his back and, with great effort, managed to pull his head backward without moving his spine, basically looking up from his torso.

The original physician had instructed Jack not to lift his head, yet the problems that ensued went beyond Jack's inability to flex or extend his neck. Looking over his shoulder while driving was impossible: By turning with his whole torso, he used his eyes to compensate for the absence of rotation in his neck. Walking up and down stairs was also extremely difficult because the improper alignment of Jack's body parts threw him off balance. Once you have held your head rigidly in a certain position, it is difficult to find your center of gravity.

A feeling of balance in your body results from energy flowing through the musculature, thus enabling the bony components to move in proper relationship. Being balanced is directly connected to your ability to move your body with relative effortlessness. Any part that is fixated and immobilized detracts from your body's overall functioning. My work with Jack went considerably beyond releasing the rigidity in his neck. He learned how hard the rest of his body had worked throughout the years to keep his neck from moving. Jack learned that what he had thought was a neck problem had come to be a body problem.

MOVEMENT: A GRADUAL AWAKENING

In a given yoga stretch, you may actually feel the discomfort of stretching a body part—for example, your lower back—that has not moved for weeks, months, or years. When chronic tension is stretched, the feeling may not be completely pleasant, as was the case for Jack in the early stages of our work together. If you learn to tolerate this feeling, however, you can make great strides toward being able to move your body in a more positive direction. This is often how it works: You get a catch or a tight spot in your body. Perhaps you begin to notice a place in your breathing that feels stuck and sore. At this point, you hold yourself back from the movement that exacerbates the pain. Sometimes medically oriented practitioners reinforce this response by recommending bed rest, neck braces, inactivity, painkillers, or antidepressants.

Your body has amazing powers to heal itself. Conscious movement allows for this type of healing. Typically, you would not stumble upon these abilities accidentally. A mentor or coach can help guide you to discover and implement these skills. For myself, my ability to relax deliberately, realign my body at will, and find relief from tension and pain through movement has come from years of training, practice, and research. To this day, I appreciate professional help when I find I'm working through a difficult holding pattern. Rolfing and yoga are two natural approaches in which you learn to listen to your body on an ongoing basis. The feedback has always been there, but you may have learned to ignore it. It is often a matter of learning to hear the feedback and decipher the message. You can learn to move differently from the inside in order to resolve structural problems associated with misalignment, pain, or discomfort. Paying attention to and being aware of your body can at first be a slight distraction from your daily routine, but with practice, you can learn to stay tuned in to the sensations in your body while keeping your mind and senses also focused on whatever activity is at hand.

Faye is a nurse and a hospice volunteer. In addition to feeling the emotional stress of her work, she drives for several hours each day to the homes of her patients. She often must physically handle large, bedridden patients. By the time Faye began her Rolfing and stretching, she had been suffering from back pain for twenty years. In the first several weeks of being Rolfed, Faye found that she needed to be constantly aware of breathing into her back, moving efficiently, and releasing tension. As many of us do, she would notice herself tensing her back in response to fatigue and stress. And although this may be a common response, for Faye it was especially critical that she learn to manage her back in response to stress. For her back, the constant holding was too much abuse.

The debilitation from which Faye suffered was disrupting her functioning at work. She worked with families dealing with grief, anger, and other intense emotions. As a direct result of this intensity, Faye had learned throughout the years to "brace herself" for protection. She realized that the way in which she protected herself had become a liability. By guarding and separating herself from her environment, she had unwittingly created a situation that was even more threatening to her own well-being, and one that exacerbated the chronic physical problems along her spine.

Faye began to realize that her back required constant vigilance and observation. She gradually saw that her back pain was the manifestation of her response to many events in her life, both professional and personal. When Faye had broken up with her boyfriend, her back had gone into a significant spasmodic episode. Faye had been unable to communicate her feelings. She dealt with the situation by simply cutting off her relationship with him, assuming physically and emotionally a rigid position.

For about the first six weeks or so into the Rolfing process, staying aware of her back became Faye's preoccupation. Occasionally she felt even more tired by the end of the day, because of the new focus of her attention. She needed to take care not only of her patients, but of herself as well. Like Faye, if you are doing this work, you might find yourself temporarily trading in chronic tension for fatigue or even exhaustion. There is a profound relief associated with letting go of old and intense holding patterns. And occasionally, like Faye, you may feel a great need to sleep during this transition period. But as Faye discovered, containing the energy that comes from the release of intense and chronic muscular holding becomes much easier with time. Gradually Faye learned to live with more energy. She learned that it is okay to move through life without protecting herself from or bracing herself against some imaginary calamity.

PUTTING IT TOGETHER

Working with an educator who inculcates her understanding of living fully in the physical body is important to your realization of specific goals and achievement of certain necessary personal changes. As magical and powerful as Rolfing and yoga are, people don't automatically release their holding patterns unless they are effectively educated to do so.

When you begin Rolfing or yoga, do not attempt to force the release (actually a contradiction in terms) of blocked energy and tension in your body. Positive benefits come from *allowing* the release. It is natural for you to become acutely aware of precisely how it feels to hold your body tense. Rolfing is a process for getting out the tension that you didn't know you had. Knowing what you are doing and how you are doing it when you feel yourself tense up should be regarded as progress. That awareness is a vital first step in the process of becoming more responsible and in charge of your body. Allow yourself time to integrate what you learn about your body through Rolfing and yoga into your life. It takes more time to stay with this part of the process and regard it as valuable, than it does to "hurry up and let it all go."

Rolfers are trained to work with the client's breathing. Particularly during the more intense moments of being Rolfed, you will find that focusing on your breath allows more energy to flow into the constricted tissue. The increase of oxygen that comes with a fuller breath also helps to open your body. For many years I have asked my clients to imagine their bodies expanding with the inhalation, and then the tension being carried out by the exhalation. Whether through this visualization, or simply allowing your body to become calm and relaxed while you follow your breath, the same principle can be applied in yoga.

Pranayama literally means "breath control." This discipline entails a variety of breathing exercises that energize the body and that quiet and center the mind. These exercises often complement meditation and yoga. Prana (breath) is the life force. The more full and expansive your breath, the more life energy you experience. Pranayama is a metaphysical science with its roots in basic biology and chemistry. Every cell in our bodies needs oxygen in order to live and thrive. You will find that the more you consistently breathe fully, the more energy you have. Filling yourself up with your breath, then, enhances the objectives of Rolfing and yoga. It is easier to breathe when your body is relaxed and to relax when your body is breathing.

Muscles that have been shortened and made tense throughout the years have lost their elasticity and their natural fluid content. Dehydration of the muscle tissue is a by-product of chronic tension and immobilization. This can occur in the matrix of blood-rich muscle tissue, and in connective tissue, and the abundant variety of tendons and ligaments that are ubiquitous in your body's structure. Several words describe this phenomenon: calcification, fibrosis, adhesions, fixations, and contractions. In this situation, soft tissue hardens, compresses, and becomes less pliable. Associated with these occurrences are joint stiffness, muscular tightness, limited range of motion, pain, discomfort, low energy, and chronic fatigue. Certain psychological conditions, such as chronic depression, are also related to fixations in the body's structural patterns.

This may seem like a formidable list of problems. It is the "stuff" of the work of a Rolfer or a yoga teacher. When the manipulations and ministrations are done consciously and deliberately, miracles seem to occur. I have learned to never underestimate the power of deep relaxation, because I see it manifest significant physiological changes every day that I work.

* * * * *

Connective tissue, or fascia, is the matrix with which Rolfers work. It is the strong and sensitive material inside the body that connects, binds, separates, and supports the individual contents of the body. If I am working on a client's feet and he tightens his jaw, I can feel the connective tissue being pulled where my hands are. If I have used too much pressure, I can see and feel the entire body, through the connective tissue, recoil as a body does when it withdraws from pain. It behooves me to support the client to work with and release the intensity. I can do this by encouraging the client to breathe, pacing the work, lightening my touch, and offering verbal cues to help him release tension. The point is, I need to create an environment that is relatively stress free in order to get good results from the work. If the client feels that the work is too difficult, then the results will be lost to the effort and contraction in his body. Said another way, I will have a better outcome of the work on the feet if the client's entire body has relaxed and moved into an expansive state. It takes rapport and trust between Rolfer and client to work in this manner.

Yoga is most effectively approached in the same way. Aggressiveness can work against the inherent benefits of yoga. Certainly the accomplishment of a difficult yoga asana requires stamina and focus. But, it works best, while stretching your body, to concentrate on letting go while you move carefully into the areas where you feel some intensity. The feeling of tightness or stiffness in your body is the information we work with in yoga; it is not bad news. In fact, I frequently remind my students that discovery of the dense and stiff areas in their musculature is a valuable accomplishment. On a physical level, the goal of yoga is to uncover and move past those areas in the muscles that are unyielding. My sense when I am stretching and perceive a tightness across my back is, Oh, there's that spot I've been feeling! Now I can stretch and release it. It is much more difficult to let go of the holding in your body if you can't tell exactly where it is and precisely how it feels to hang on there. Yoga enables you to directly experience tension in your body so you know just what you are working with. The pleasure that moves into your body as you deliberately release the tightness that you experience in the asana is a rush of energy and relief. Any discomfort that you may have felt is washed away in the relaxation that shortly follows.

The sensation of stretching a stiff muscle can be intense, without necessarily being unpleasant or painful–unless it is overdone or forced. In this way, stretching is much akin to the experience of being Rolfed. The muscle tissue responds favorably to direct pressure, stretching, and heat. The tight muscle or muscle groups have a reduced blood supply. The tightness itself prevents arterial blood from bringing nutrients, including oxygen, to the muscle. With the decreased circulation, the venous return to the heart is also diminished. In the muscle tissue itself, there is a depletion of fresh oxygen, whose job it is to carry out the waste products that build up from the chronic tension. The deep pressure of Rolfing and the stretch of yoga bring an influx of blood and a loosening of the muscle's grip. A deep relaxation follows. This is such a profound relief for your body, indeed such a pleasurable experience, that the pain does not register in the way that pain normally would. It feels incredibly good to let go.

Rolfing and yoga are educational processes. Everything you learn about your body enables you to be more aware of your body. Your Rolfer or your yoga teacher may be the catalyst for you to make these important discoveries. Learning that positive changes in your body come from within, however, is the ultimate goal of this education.

3

Chapter **THREE**

Rolfing, Then and Now

Up until the past fifteen years or so, Rolfers were trained to hold their bodies in particular ways. This posture featured a series of specific holding patterns which were considered "correct" at the time: the arms were turned in with the elbows bent out, the head was held on top, and the lumbar spine was pressed back slightly. (See figure 3.1.) During approximately this same time period, yoga teachers were giving the same instructions to their students. I remember my teachers' training at the Iyengar Yoga Institute and my trips to India to study with B. K. S. Iyengar in the late 1970s. In those days we tucked our tailbones under and lifted our ribs incessantly. Rolfers were teaching the same deliberation in posture during the same time period.

As a member of both groups, I see how each has changed its outlook regarding proper alignment of the pelvis and the lumbar spine. Professionals who understand structure now more commonly accept a comfortable lumbar curve. Yoga instructors and Rolfers are also more familiar with the concept of gravitational support. We no longer think we have to hold ourselves "correctly," which is an impossible thing to do.

Not only are Rolfing and yoga complementary in present time, they have taken a similar journey through history. The outcome of this story is that yoga and Rolfing continue to promote body alignment, albeit with a more modern, informed view.

Occasionally I meet someone who believes that Rolfing is an agonizing, coercive method and that anyone who wants to get Rolfed must be a bit masochistic and needs his head examined. These notions usually come from people who were Rolfed twenty years ago or who knew someone who was Rolfed back then. The work used to be much more heavy-handed and aggressive than it is today.

Figure 3.1: Arms turned in, head held on top, pelvis slightly tilted.

Two decades ago, many people associated Rolfing with pain but also with terrific results. For this reason, Rolfing survived, despite a rather bad public review when it was originally introduced. The early period of Rolfing extended from the late 1950s through the mid-1970s. My first ten Rolfing sessions in 1973 were very painful. To this day, I am often amazed that I could have been so enamored of work that was practically unbearable. Upon further reflection, however, I always recall that the discomfort was a small price to pay for the freedom and positive feelings I gained in my body, functionally and emotionally.

The 1970s were an important era in the movement to realize human potential. Masses of people joined together to follow Werner Erhard, the Maharishi Mahesh Yogi, Leonard Orr, and Ram Dass. More and more people began consciously and actively "working on themselves." During this time, Fritz Perls (of Gestalt therapy) and Ida Rolf were at Esalen Institute in Big Sur, California. People went there from all over the country to be Rolfed and to learn Gestalt therapy. Werner Erhard and his trainers hurled derogatory epithets at the est participants and said they needed to wake up and move on in their lives. And all of this was going on at a time when Rolfing hurt like hell. Many followers were involved in more than one of these approaches during that period.

Historically speaking, all of this held meaning. Imagine our culture as an enormous sleeping giant, collectively unconscious as a people and relatively unaware of who we were. A loud wake-up call may well have been appropriate. I'm not implying that, as an est graduate myself, being insulted by Erhard's hit men was necessary for my evolution, but it did get my attention. Likewise, my first Rolfer in 1973 may have had a real "divide and conquer" attitude toward my body, but despite the brutality, Rolfing produced definite and positive results. I like the fact that I was part of this movement twenty years ago. It gives me a certain perspicacity on the evolution and sophistication in the field of personal growth. I've seen many of the changes in the field first-hand.

We no longer need the drama, the flamboyance, or the aggression that was part of the growth-oriented culture of the early 1970s. Outstanding contemporary leaders in the fields of psychology, body therapy, self-development, and medicine give us a new paradigm for our approach to ourselves and our regard for our own evolution. Several key figures who have had the greatest impact on my view of my self and my relationship to my work are Bernie Siegel, Arny Mindell, Ken Wilber and the late Treya Killam Wilber, and Peter Levine. I believe that the models that are being taught have changed because of the dramatic increase in the sheer numbers of individuals involved in the human potential movement.

In the hundredth-monkey theory, after a critical number of monkeys learn an important survival skill, all of the monkeys en masse acquire the new behavior. In terms of human culture, there comes a point where "everybody gets it." As opportunities for self-growth have become abundant and easily accessible, many people have plugged in. In psychological terms, this is the collective conscious mind. I relate this to Rolfing and yoga because these are two arenas where you can learn about yourself in relationship to the other members of the Earth community. By releasing mental and physical blocks that have served to keep you separate from others, you will see yourself in a different light: as a part of a global network.

In present time, a Rolfing session may seem considerably more gentle than the heavy-handed style of two decades ago. In addition to being manipulated during a Rolfing session, you may feel touched, or moved, in nonphysical ways. Frequently this occurs in conjunction with deep relaxation, which is an altered state of consciousness. You may have insights about how you are wired, as your body reveals certain emotional pockets of tension or strain. These realizations, or *ahas*, often emerge from deep within the body. At times, these emotions come unlocked quietly, subtly, and with no fanfare. But, if you shift into a heightened state of self-awareness and self-understanding, the results in your private life may be dramatic. An old stimulus may bring about a completely new response. While under stress, you may find that you can still breathe and allow your shoulders to soften, despite the intensity in your immediate environment, despite the fact that you feel that you are being provoked. *This is where the true emotional release is measured: right in the middle of everyday life.*

What happens on the table during the session is often exciting. But, histrionics do not reveal the degree to which you have cleared yourself of emotional baggage. Jill, a client of mine a number of years ago, went from Rolfer to therapist to Rolfer in our community. No one, including myself, seemed to be able to effectively support Jill in moving ahead in her personal development—either through body therapy or through psychotherapy. And the problems in Jill's life were a relentless reminder of her inability to cope on even the most basic level.

Jill cried easily during treatments. If I was working on her belly, she would let out deep wails, often sounding like a wounded animal. At first I was tempted to think, Oh, this is great. This woman really knows how to release. That illusion did not last long, however, as it quickly became apparent that she was not releasing her pain at all. Rather, she was hanging on to whatever it was that kept her life so shut down. The big emotional scenes were really a cover-up for a deep, carefully guarded pain inside. Jill emoted, but she did not improve. I can't help but wonder if I would have better success with Jill now than I did six years ago.

Many people decide to get Rolfed because they appreciate the idea that their bodies store past emotional hurts. Through Rolfing, they hope to get relief from pain. People expect that their lives might work better if they learn to let go of the holding in their bodies, even if the cause of the tension is psychological. The release of physical tension *is* a step in the right direction. Rolfing *is* about personal freedom. But each individual requires different steps to achieve this liberation, depending on the particular issues to be dealt with.

In the late 1970s and a bit into the 1980s, I believed that a person should have a nice, big, volatile, thrashing experience on the table during the Rolfing session itself, in order to benefit from the "emotional release" of Rolfing. After all, didn't we learn from Primal Screaming that the more hysterical we were—the more our feelings were "out there"–the more value we were getting? This is a bit tongue-in-cheek, but it was essentially the prevailing attitude ten to fifteen years ago. I have since learned that emotions can release more slowly, like air from a tire that has a tiny puncture. Emotions need not explode, nor is there a need for a big show. There is nothing inherently valuable in re-experiencing a trauma. Once is enough. In fact, there is a distinct advantage to releasing in a more mild-mannered way. If you are able to remain naturally calm, often the repressed or stored information simply slips away.

Many of my clients are looking for release of the emotions that are stored or blocked in their bodies. I advise them not to be too attached to an emotional release during the session, mostly for the reasons just mentioned. But there is more to it. If a person expects to thrash about, or to cry hysterically, then he will miss what may be an even more appropriate and subtle way of letting go of past wounds. Let's imagine that the area where the person feels a need to release is in the belly, and the emotion is anger. The person need not experience the anger directly. On a psychic level, the tension associated with the anger can be simply released. The tension literally disappears as the rest of the body adapts to an increased flow of energy and relaxation around the belly. In fact, the opening and softening of the abdomen and the positive feelings associated with that have a more profound impact than the re-experiencing of anger. This is the new way in which the individual experiences this part of his body.

4
5

NO PAIN, NO GAIN?

Some Rolfers certainly touch more heavily than others do. Fortunately, the work is creative enough to lend itself to a Rolfer's personal interpretation. Throughout the years, I have spent countless hours contemplating this pain issue, and it has become obvious to me that I am working against myself if my clients are in extreme stress because of the pain. Relaxing is difficult for a client in great pain. Rolfing, if it is anything, is a system for allowing any stress in the body to be released. If the work is too intense, then the client will contract, thereby putting more stress into his body.

Some pain, as we say, "hurts good." The client experiences the feeling as acceptable, agreeable, and perhaps even desirable. He can stay present and relaxed mentally. He can observe the work with his mind without needing to split himself off from his body. His mind is not going berserk. His body receives the work, even though it may be intense. The client *wants* to have that experience. In this case, the client does not spend precious energy attempting to keep the feelings in his body outside of his experience. If the client can expand with the pressure, he has reversed the tides of his typical response to stress.

4

Chapter FOUR

Yoga: A New Twist

The popularity of yoga has crossed class, gender, age, race, professional status, and nationality. In my community, there are classes for athletes, children, senior citizens, pregnant women, bodyworkers, actors, and corporate officers. Apparently, word is out that this is a marvelous thing. As an ancient art form that enjoys current popularity, yoga is here to stay.

Why this popularity? Two recent articles help to explain. One was in *Newsweek*.

> We are moving from the perception that yoga is an esoteric, far out type of religious activity to what it really is: a practice that is both mental and physical....Why is yoga on the rise? Because stress is, too.[1]

The other article was in the *San Francisco Examiner*, the most widely distributed newspaper in my area.

> If the 80s were the decade of "no pain, no gain," then the fitness craze of the 90s can be measured by the mantra "There's no place like om." Yoga has come down off its mountain. It's the newest, hippest health fad—and it's 4,000 years old....With its mix of acrobatic stretching and serene meditation, yoga for many has become the perfect, low impact workout, exercising both body and mind, a tonic to the 9-to-5 grind. Yoga...is becoming increasingly accepted by some physicians who believe it can play an important role in combating the plague of modern life: stress. In fact, doctors say, most common stress-reduction techniques are derived from yoga.[2]

Significant evidence indicates that yoga is capable of reversing or offsetting some of the deleterious side effects of aging and unhealthful living. In *Reversing Heart Disease*, Dr. Dean Ornish of Sausalito, California, explains some brilliant and original ideas about sickness and disease. He maintains that isolation can lead to stress and, ultimately, to illness, whereas intimacy can be healing.

> Although many people think of yoga only as a collection of various stretching exercises and postures to limber up the body, it is more than that. Yoga also includes breathing techniques, meditation, visualization, progressive relaxation

practices, self-analysis, and altruism. All of these different methods, though, have a common purpose: to heal our isolation.[3]

Yoga feels incredibly good. Sometimes I joke with my students by telling them that the essence of yoga is hedonism. Yoga is also serious, intense work at times. But the benefits are numerous, and the results are long lasting. I'll use myself as an example. With enormous demands on my time and energy, my body gets put to the test every day. I work intensively, care for our children, and, together with my husband, manage our home. Like many people, I am faced daily with life's inevitable curveballs. Physical exercise and yoga are an essential part of my daily routine. I wouldn't expect to feel as strong, fit, and comfortable as I do in my body if I didn't have this program in place. Especially when I cannot change my external environment (people, events, and circumstances), I feel power and relief from taking charge of my *internal* experience. Yoga is my lifesaver. Having practiced diligently for more than twenty years, I believe in it wholeheartedly.

You may find yourself drawn to yoga for many reasons. I list these motives in the preface of this book. They can be divided into categories: physical, emotional, psychological, and spiritual.

1. *Physical objectives.* We find the attainment of strength, flexibility, and endurance, the clearing up of diseases and stress-related illness, and the handling and release of chronic tension and pain in the physical category. The peacefulness that frequently results from a yoga practice creates an internal environment that is more responsive to resolving health issues. This is especially true for the disease or disorder with an emotional or psychological root, but it also applies to other types of medical problems.

   I have worked with individuals who have sought out yoga after being diagnosed with cancer, for example. By learning to relax, they feel they gain control of their bodies. One of the dreadful aspects of being diagnosed with a potentially fatal illness is the feeling of being helpless to do anything about one's health. Through yoga, these patients develop greater sensitivity toward and attunement with their own bodies. As a result, they feel they can become more involved in and more in charge of their healing process.

Through breathing and stretching, you naturally develop a sense of knowing what your body needs and wants. It is easiest to regain your health and well-being by listening to your body in a quiet and receptive frame of mind. I often remind my yoga students during savasana (the pose of complete relaxation; see part 2) that these ten minutes or so may be the quietest and most valuable time of their entire day.

2. *Emotional objectives.* These include releasing fear or grief, opening the heart chakra, learning to be calm, and discharging injuries from past trauma and abuse. A woman recovering from a painful divorce, for example, would fit into this category. Yoga would help her to feel more calm. The physical body and the emotional body are interwoven. By releasing physical tension she could release a significant amount of emotional blockage that gets stored in the body. I personally find yoga very calming to my emotional body.

3. *Psychological objectives.* In this category is the relief from personality disorders, phobias, and nervous breakdowns. The roots of such problems are often related to chronic hypertonic muscles and the associated aberrations in behavior. To be so full of tension as to feel a lack of control over one's body can lead to psychological imbalances. Here is another place, then, where the release of physical stiffness can modify an individual's psyche, behavior, and perceptions of his environment.

4. *Spiritual objectives.* On this level, you learn through yoga to view your practice as a time to raise your consciousness, to learn about and experience deeper aspects of yourself, and to evolve more fully. Through yoga, you pay attention to the aspects of life that enhance your own self-development. For example, you might discover when you resist, what it feels like, and what exactly you do when you resist. If you often resist, coming face-to-face with this side of yourself becomes a

major stepping-stone to changing your behavior. After a successful confrontation, the results appear in real life. You find yourself more inclined to go with the flow of people and events around you. This is the ultimate measure of the value of your spiritual and yoga practice: knowing what you have learned and how to implement the lessons.

* * * * *

The uninitiated may think that I am oversimplifying by ascribing so many exciting benefits to relaxation of the physical body. On the contrary, I have learned not to *underestimate* the effects of relaxation on physical and mental health. Relaxation of the body and mind can help many so-called psychological diseases and problems. Learning to release the physical and mental tension that inevitably accompany an anxiety attack can eventually help overcome such episodes.

When tension goes untreated, it can become a problem of overwhelming magnitude. By the time the patient feels totally out of control, the tension has escalated into a problem too great for the patient to deal with on his own. It actually may develop into a medical problem, such as a herniated disc, a series of migraine headaches, or irritable bowel syndrome. But the root of many of these conditions is untreated muscular tension and the concomitant emotional disturbance that often develops.

Psychiatrists and other medical doctors, recognizing the benefits of relaxation, often prescribe yoga, deep breathing, and relaxation techniques to their patients. Dr. Dean Ornish includes a daily program of yoga stretches as part of the regimen to be followed by his heart patients.[4] He has made history with his program for reversing heart disease. His scientific method works without drugs and without surgery. In *Reversing Heart Disease*, Dr. Ornish writes,

During times of perceived danger, all of your muscles begin to clench and contract as a way of fortifying your "body armor" so that you are more protected during a fight. During times of chronic stress, your muscles may become chronically tensed. After a while, this may lead to neck pain, a sore back, or discomfort in your shoulders. Learning to stretch and lengthen muscles that are chronically contracted helps to rebalance your body and your mind.[5]

Successful and impressive work has been done with schizophrenic patients through yoga and breathing techniques. The breath is always included in the focus of the yoga practitioner. This is done during the asanas, or yoga poses, as well as during a meditation. For the schizophrenic or otherwise psychotic individual, focusing on the breath enables him to deal with a chaotic energy situation. Whether in response to drugs or to some kind of internal breakdown, a smooth flow of energy moving through the organism has been severely disrupted. Yoga and breath control help facilitate a return to the state of balance and equilibrium.[6]

Learning to move through life with more flexibility, equanimity, and fluidity is an important series of events. Metaphorically, these changes enable you to be more responsive and less reactive to your environment. Being flexible comes in handy when life seems challenging and constantly changing. Through yoga, you learn how to roll with the punches.

Through the asanas, you learn to move your body in ways that simply do not present themselves in your normal course of daily activities. Your range of motion, particularly if you are sedentary, utilizes one tiny fraction of the movement potential in your body. If your body is stiff and habitually held in a tense fashion, then the range through which you move becomes even more compromised. Through yoga you discover new ways to loosen and move your body and, consequently, new ways to express yourself.

Imagine an individual who is unable to delight in the exchange that occurs between people when their hearts are open to giving and receiving love. For someone who has extreme tension around his heart, who has shut off the energy flow around his chest, arms, and upper back, a loving embrace or even a hug may be physically painful or impossible or psychologically threatening. Have you ever hugged someone who was unable to receive your hug or hug you back? For some people, this is a chronic, pervasive problem that shows up in the way the musculature is organized throughout the body. Imagine the high price for this kind of tension in terms of the restraints it places on the individual. Releasing the chronic armoring around the arms, shoulders, and chest is a perfect example of how yoga gives you more options in your body and, consequently, in your life.

YOGA AND ROLF MOVEMENT

I had been practicing and teaching yoga for about twelve years when I began my Rolf movement training in 1983. This training has transformed the bodywork I do, and has had an enormous effect on my movement work in general and my yoga teaching in particular.

Again and again my teachers would talk about support: how the ground supports you when you stand and walk; how the Rolfing table supports you when you are prone; how your pelvis supports your upper body as you move; how your legs support you when you run; how the Earth supports you when you live and breathe. Ultimately, I learned, our bodies support us to move through life in a way that yields maximum pleasure, balance, and satisfaction.

Recently I was teaching a class entitled "Yoga and Rolf Movement." At the end of class, I guided the students through a progressive relaxation. As I watched these students in their bodies, I saw varying degrees of surrender and relaxation. It was obvious to me that some students were more capable than others of relaxing their physical bodies, *of allowing the mat and the floor to*

5
3

support them. It dawned on me that issues regarding support may stem from a very early time in people's lives, perhaps even infancy. As I have worked with this concept with groups and individuals, I have come to feel that there is substance to it. I say this based on the fact that people are moved deeply as they explore these areas.

What I discovered in class that day has to do with the ways in which we may have felt unsafe and unsupported in our bodies when we were tiny. I began thinking about how much of the chronic tension that plagues us originates in ways we learned to hold ourselves when we were little. As I observed the students on the floor, I saw the unique way in which each one held his body. These holding patterns were highly individualized and ingrained in the way each person expressed himself through his body. Any difficulty relaxing in savasana is merely a reflection of the person's difficulty in relaxing in a variety of life experiences.

For many of us, trusting our environment enough to let go is a risky and potentially threatening ordeal. For whatever reasons, there were times when we were babies when it did not seem safe to let go, to not hold on, to trust and relax and feel that there was ample support for our tiny bodies and our precious psyches to expand and release. Given the proliferation in the media of stories of rampant child abuse—emotional, physical, and sexual—we can easily imagine a number of painful experiences that may leave a small child feeling threatened.

As tiny persons having few survival skills, we were limited to crying, withdrawing, and bracing our bodies with protective armoring. The ways in which we store tension forty years later mirror the decisions we made when we were small. This is why it is risky business to let go, in present time, as adults. If we allow ourselves the experience of receiving support from within our own bodies, and from our immediate physical environments, *something had better be there to hold us when we stop holding ourselves.*

An effective way for me to provide this support to someone who is suffering from chronic tension or pain is to place my hands on the part of the body that is holding: the shoulder, the abdomen, the neck, the leg, and so on. The person can be lying down on the table, standing up, or sitting down. I touch the person in a way that conveys my presence and my willingness to hold him. I even say, "Perhaps you don't have to hold yourself here. I'm willing and able to hold you here," or, "Allow me to support your shoulder. Can you hand your shoulder over to me," or, "Only one of us needs to hold your shoulder. Can I be the one to hold your shoulder?" These cues are powerful; they convey to the individual that if he lets go, he will get the support he needs. He will not be in a free fall, without support. Appealing to the simple mentality of the tiny child, I tell the person, "If you let go, you will still be safe. I will not let you fall; you will not get hurt. Nothing bad will happen. I will support you. I am able and willing to hold you." These techniques often produce astonishing results.

Utilizing the principles of support in yoga is natural. Because we put ourselves through such a wide variety of stretches and movement sequences, we are constantly changing our relationship to the Earth within the gravitational field. Each asana puts on our bodies a different demand to let go, so we develop the ability to surrender to gravity in a 360-degree sphere. Gravity is "under" our feet when we stand, but it is "under" our buttocks when we sit down and "under" our bellies when we lie face down. Our bodies learn to accept support in three dimensions. It is the multidimensional release, the combination of all of the releases, that allows the opening to move into our cores, into the centers of our beings. In this way, the changes are not superficial. They occur at a level where we can feel a significant difference in the quality of our experience of living in our bodies.

5

Chapter FIVE

Getting It in My Body

The title of this chapter reflects the way in which I use my own body as an experimental laboratory for the therapeutic and teaching work that I do with clients and students. If I am working with a client who has back problems, for example, the way in which I live in my back—how my back moves and breathes and supports me—becomes pertinent in the work I do. More than the touch of my hands and the words I use are being transmitted. If you can think of people as energetic beings whose bodies telegraph the state of their strength, including blocks, flows, surges, and restrictions, it becomes easy to see how much we humans communicate with our bodies. Because of the intimate nature of this work, the practitioner and client influence each other strongly.

If my client is dealing with chronic fatigue, I will either be sucked into his exhaustion because of my own tiredness or I will model for him someone who has plenty of energy and functions well. Another client may present shortness of breathing, an asthmatic response to unresolved trauma from his childhood. Again, if I know how to breathe in spite of fear and tension, I can be empathetic without losing my effectiveness or professional posture. If my client lives with chronic tension, my ability to work effectively with this person is a function of my knowing how to relax my own body.

This is not to suggest that Rolfers, yoga teachers, and other therapists must have perfect bodies in order to work effectively with clients. Assuming responsibility for our own bodies, resolving personal health issues, and managing our own stress enable us to practice what we preach. There is an old saying, 'We teach what we need to learn'. That may be true, but I believe that we teach best that which we have already mastered.

As professionals, living consciously in our bodies does not mean that we have arrived. On the contrary, living consciously is a *process* through which we continuously refine our skills, learning and relearning our lessons. Through this process we become models for our clients, as much for our accomplishments as for our work efforts. For example, when I get a stiff neck, it feels like I am receiving a lesson in breathing and spinal mechanics. Although they are not particularly pleasant, I make the most from these lessons. Among other benefits, I gain empathy for my clients. The process of resolving my own stiff neck definitely improves the work I do with other people's bodies.

I worked last year with a woman named Laura. At the same time that she was being Rolfed, Laura was also taking yoga classes and spending quite a bit of time learning to open her body. She was separated from her husband and dealing with her own frustrations about not feeling capable of accepting love into her life. She perceived a physical block in her chest that she believed was part of the problem. Her body told the story of her psychic pain. The tension itself reflected the inner conflict and resistance Laura experienced in this relationship.

My response to a person who is struggling with a lack of self-love is to open my own heart to that person. It felt to me that part of the therapy with Laura entailed my supporting her as she explored, cautiously at first, these feelings she had kept sealed shut around her heart center. How could I possibly do that if my own heart were closed? Our conversations frequently touched on love, marriage, and relationships. I did not consider myself an expert in these topics, but I did feel that modeling the part of myself that contains love, that is not afraid of intimacy, was part of our work together. This is more subtle than my saying, Okay, Laura, now I will show you what it is like to feel my heart be open. We exchanged information in the context of our relationship and the closeness that developed as we worked together.

Whatever I perceive in my own body, I am able to communicate with my body, mind, and spirit. As I was with Laura, she was being loved. I stayed focused and present as she practiced receiving and staying open. Of course, I was not Laura's husband, and certainly the dynamics were different. But Laura and her husband did get back together toward the end of her Rolfing, and Laura had glowing reports about how good her body felt, particularly in light of her having allowed love in. She got it in *her* body. In terms of my effectiveness as her Rolfer, it helped me to stay in my own body, feeling my feelings, and allowing my heart to be open.

DEEP WORK, OR ENERGY WORK?

I have already mentioned that Rolfing was aggressive and more heavy-handed in the 1970s. The work has been refined and modified considerably since Dr. Rolf's death in 1979. Without the aggression and the force, we get better results. The client is *invited* to release whatever he is holding, not forced to do so. I am able to achieve results with my clients in part as a result of the work I have received from other skillful professionals who have helped me to release tension and aggression from my body. By virtue of the fact that I have worked diligently to release significant amounts of resistance in my body, I can approach another person, a client, without the hard push and force that might otherwise be a problem for me. If my body and my client's body are fields of energy, then I am entering his field with minimum resistance in my field. Working in this manner enables me to utilize the energy flowing through my body as a tool.

I observed a student Rolfer in one of my workshops recently. Her body was stiff and inflexible. Her work produced significant discomfort for the Rolfer with whom she was working. Even after the recipient made many requests for the woman to back off, to use less pressure, the Rolfer had a difficult time connecting with the recipient *energetically* and working with the recipient toward greater release. It was obvious to me that the Rolfer doing the work had no internal representation of release, support, or energy flow. Never having learned to live in her body in a way that allowed for this kind of freedom, she had available to her to work with only the tools of pressure and resistance. Learning new hands-on techniques would have missed the mark. What finally did work for this particular individual was the stretching, breathing, and relaxation that we did throughout the workshop. Once she experienced release and freedom in her own body, she understood what her model was asking for when he asked her to use less force in her work with his body.

A therapist whose body is unwieldy must use more pressure to facilitate a release in the client's body. If energy isn't moving in the practitioner's body, if her body is chronically stiff and rigid, then she can't move energy in another person's body, except by pressure and force, which is the state of her own internal energetic flow. In this case, there is a risk that the body therapy would become a battleground, with the hands of the therapist pushing hard against the resistance in the client's body and with the client pushing back, equally hard. *The resistance in the client's body increases in this scenario.* This is analogous to a psychotherapist trying hard to force the client to change. It doesn't work.

I gave and received bodywork sessions by pushing hard like this in years past. I remember them vividly. They were exhausting rather than energizing. After a session in which my will battled against the will of my client, I would feel as if I had been clubbed. Sometimes the client's intention to hang on seemed to be greater than my intention to facilitate a release. Furthermore, he seemed to meet any aggressive attempt on my part to "get him to let go" with more resistance.

The focus of my work has changed considerably. I no longer consider it my responsibility to "make the client relax." I understand now that it is my job to help the client see and feel how and where he is holding and then to support him through any change or release he is ready to allow. Working in this way yields better results and is more pleasurable for both of us.

I am stimulated and feel pleasure when I do my deepest work while being aware of energy flows, both my client's and my own. This comes from the rich contact I make with the client as we work *as a team* toward his unfolding. Tangible physical results—such as relief from pain, or a lessening of a scoliotic (lateral S) curve—while working with the body's energies are exciting. The therapist who works in this fashion is a conduit. Experientially, I have my own energies flowing and am able to work from *intention*, rather than from force. In order to work in this way, I must have the following:

1. physical relaxation
2. clear thoughts and objectives
3. a quiet mind
4. an acceptance of any information received from my client's body
5. a nonattachment to results
6. the ability to persevere and not get stuck even if my client's body feels stuck
7. an open heart
8. skillfulness in perceiving the blocks in my client's body
9. the ability to empower my client so that ultimately he has a sense for taking responsibility for any positive change and release
10. a highly developed sense of structure and function to facilitate the process and change on this level as well

Working in this mode further ensures that I will be able to help a client to release from the deepest possible level. This manner of working is pleasurable and energizing, because I feel it in my body each time my client releases tension and increases the flow of energy in his body. This is my fuel. This is, in part, how I communicate with my client: through our bodies. We are on the same wavelength, each having equal access to the energy moving through both of us. This then becomes less a matter of my healing the client, and more a situation in which any who are present are healed.

SHOWING BY EXAMPLE

Frequently I ask my clients to touch my body in a professional and nonsexual way in order for them to feel me do something that I am asking them to do. For example, if I am working with an individual who finds it extremely difficult to release the tension around the kneecaps, I will contract my leg in the same precise manner as the client. As I drop the patella (kneecap) down and relax my quadriceps, I ask the client to put his hand on my knee. I can say, "See? This is how you are holding your leg. Now, feel how I release my thigh muscles and my knee drops down? That is what we are working toward in your leg." This demonstration generally enables the client to gain greater control over his body; he has learned by *feeling and seeing* precisely what I am asking him to do. The more senses that are involved, the greater the chance that the client will learn.

This approach is effective when we are working toward the client's releasing the lumbar spine, the lower back. While we are sitting, I can easily model the way in which the client is out of balance. As I shift my weight toward a more balanced sitting position, I ask the client to place his hands on my sacrum, or wherever the most dramatic change occurs. As I release the tension around my sacrum, he can feel that release with his hands. A client said after working in this way that by touching my body, he learned exactly what to do in his body. The suggestions and visualizations I had made previously were no longer abstract once he had his hands on the changes.

Using my own body to demonstrate letting go and relaxing within the gravitational field is particularly useful for individuals who process information visually. Such an individual may have difficulty making a change when he has *heard* the information, or when he is asked to *feel* the release. If he can *see* me drop my shoulders down, or *see* how I contact the ground with my feet when I walk, he may understand the information more easily.

A nonspecific cue is rarely effective for someone who doesn't know that he is holding his body tightly, *especially if he doesn't know how he is doing it.* For example, "Relax your arm" often gets no results. "Notice how you are holding your arm" can be more effective. I get even better results if I encourage the client to see *that* he is holding his arm and *how* he is holding his arm, by offering support with my own hands. When I give such cues as "Let your leg rest against my leg," and "Can you allow the weight of your arm to fall into my hands?" I am using my own body, which is supported and at rest in the gravitational field, as a conduit for the client to process his own release. The client's body relaxes *through* my body.

On a psychological level, I support the client to be just the way he is. I do not try to change him. Many individuals resist tremendously when it seems that someone wants them to be different from the way they are. The harder I try to get the client to change, the more invested I become in the results, and the greater the chance that both of us will become frustrated, as if we have failed. If the client is responsible for the changes that occur in his own body, however, then the onus is off me to make certain that he lets go. The pressure is off both of us. In my experience, this is a much easier environment in which to work with my clients. We both breathe easier.

Another option in doing this kind of work is for me to frame the request using words that are specific to the desired change. Instead of "Relax your arm," I can say, "Allow the natural weight of your arm to fall down toward the table"—or something equally informative and precise. I use words to enlighten the client as to what will happen when his body softens and relaxes. This is part of the educational process. It takes practice to know how to select words that will elicit a specific response. It is my goal to speak to the client in a way that deepens his sense of his body, that raises his awareness. But I must analyze the client's behavior first, in order to address the particulars of his holding pattern from an anatomical and kinesiological/functional point of view.

An excellent method is to speak about the client's body in relation to gravity (or to the table or the floor.) If the client is holding his body, he has not allowed gravity to support his weight. Speaking in this context enables him to discover where and how he has kept his body from letting go. The trick is to figure out what he is doing, or not doing, and select my words accordingly. The more consciously I live in my own body, the more sensitive I am in facilitating consciousness in my client's body.

LANGUAGE

I pay close attention to my body language, the quality of my touch, my pace, and the words I select when I am working with groups and individuals. By living with awareness in my own body, I understand what changes occur when my body relaxes and releases its holding. By observing my own process I enable myself to tune in to my client's process with greater acuity. Perhaps that sounds paradoxical. In the classes I lead for professional bodyworkers I always ask the participants the following riddle: "How is it that your complete awareness of your own body while you are working, not only is not a distraction, but helps you in fact, to be that much more attentive to what is happening in your client's body?"

This riddle answers itself as the students begin to work. It becomes obvious that it is out of their own body and self awareness that they become sensitive to their client' bodies. Analyzing their the clients' needs with their brains is using important information, but this is not the whole picture. The rich sensory information that the practitioners find in their own bodies makes this process more complete. As I am working, for example, if I lean into my client's buttock muscles with my hand, if the muscles yield to the pressure, there is a wave of release and relaxation in my body. If the client pushes back, in effect resisting the pressure, somewhere in my body I will feel that the field of resistance has increased.

While I am working, I have a basic agreement with myself: If my body is not comfortable, I change my position immediately. Not only is my own comfort important, but in order to stay connected energetically with my client, my body must be fluid. Comfort is a measure of fluidity.

It is important to select words that will elicit a desirable response on the part of the Rolfing client or yoga student. If I am unconscious of the words I use, I am more at risk of guiding the individual away from positive change in his body. For example, if I suggest that he hold his shoulders away from his spine, chances are he will *contract* his body when following my suggestion. That is the effect of the word *hold*. Because I know that my intention is for all of the changes in his body to come as a result of some part of his body expanding, I need to use words that are consistent and congruent with that objective. If I say, "Allow more room between your shoulders and your spine," his body will most likely expand in response and do so in a way that is consistent with our overall objectives.

There is tremendous power in determining which words precisely describe what happens when my body processes a change. Likewise, it is potent to know what my body does when it is in a holding pattern. The words *squeeze* and *press*, for example, have similar connotations in the context of describing my body storing tension. But knowing whether I am squeezing or pressing may be necessary in order for me to stop doing either one. Experientially and even technically, the two words are not identical. By identifying the verb that specifies the action, I'm well on my way to change. I observe that the same is true for the people with whom I work.

Table 5.1 is entitled Verbal Cue Chart. I use this in all of my classes in advanced body therapy. This chart employs a certain fastidiousness in its language. As a user of the chart, you should recognize that just the right word can enhance your sensitivity to the nuances of your body processes.

Each word in the "Active" column is an action that causes a contraction in your body. If you do any of these actions, your body will shorten somewhere. Anywhere your body is tense, anywhere energy does not flow, you are doing something that is described by a word in this column (or a similar word that may not appear on the chart). You simply cannot lift your spine, for example, without your body shortening somewhere. The words in the "Active" column describe activities that will take your body away from resting within the gravitational field.

In the "Passive" column is a list of words that describe a variety of ways in which your body relaxes and expands. The active words describe your body working, and the passive words indicate your body parts letting go. Energy is released with the passive words; it is expended with the active words. If you ask your pelvis to float (passive) over your legs, it is practically impossible for your body to tighten in response. The beauty of using this nomenclature is that it increases the chances of producing the quality of awareness and changes you desire in your body. The passive words describe the objectives for your body in Rolfing and yoga, and active words identify the particulars of your holding patterns. Determining what your body is doing, without judging or criticizing yourself, is inherent to the success of this system.

Table 5.1: Verbal Cue Chart

	Active	*Passive*
	push	allow (e.g., breath, space, energy)
	harden	soften
	pull	drop
	force	float
	lift	fall
	compress	open
	rotate	imagine
	turn	feel
	press	free
	roll	surrender
	squeeze	release
	tense	loosen
	tighten	yield
Energy:	expended	released
Effort:	medium to high	no effort

One of my favorite cues to give a client is to ask him to walk across the floor, letting his muscles hang from his bones. I do a great imitation of a sack of bones. The client can see what I am asking him to do after watching me move in this way. This way of working (modeling and then observing) keeps me present as well as enhances my contact and working relationship with the client. My body is the most reliable source of information I have. It also is the most effective tool for teaching others to live successfully in their bodies.

6
9

6

Chapter SIX

The Energy Body

When I touch people, I touch not only their physical bodies, but their energy bodies as well. Even a skeptic can experience—as a result of effective body therapy—having energy move into a limb that has been stagnant and stuck. Even the uninitiated will spontaneously select words that are consistent with professional nomenclature to describe their bodies after being Rolfed or after doing yoga. A person may use adjectives such as *tingling, flowing,* and *vibrating* to describe what he feels. He may say that his legs feel lighter and his entire body feels more connected. For the individual who is normally disconnected from his body, these sensations are significant. This is the process through which the person reowns his body. He may have been split off or in some way disassociated from his body through tension in his musculature or breathing. He may have ignored his body by "living in his head."

Sometimes when a client struggles to find the right words to tell me what he is experiencing, I encourage him not to worry about communicating to me. It is more beneficial for him to have this pure sensation without needing to externalize it; I can see what is happening without his verbalizing it.

Metaphysics become normal to people who study and practice Rolfing and yoga and credible to the novice experiencing these events for the first time. When a client says he feels low in energy, he is actually describing a state of being that is measurable and palpable. A trained professional feels something different when she touches someone whose energy is depleted, than when she touches someone who contains an abundance of life force: It is like the difference between touching a tabletop and touching the ground. Aliveness is a form of energy that can be palpated. Many people report gaining more energy from their involvement in Rolfing or yoga. As a body shifts from being rigid, pressurized, and contracted to being supple, expansive, and relaxed, it gains flowing, vital energy. It takes a lot of work—a lot of energy—to hold tension in the musculature. When the muscles rest, the energy is readily available, and you can modify in a positive manner how it feels to live in your body, thus altering your experience of life itself.

To a large extent, your emotions determine how the energy flows in your body. Feeling exuberant and exhilarated is different physiologically than feeling sad and depressed. Furthermore, your emotions, attitudes, and other states of consciousness affect your nervous and immune systems. In an extreme case, your emotions can so greatly affect your immune system that they have an impact on your general tendency toward living or dying.[1] Chronic illness is often a side effect of chronic depression. The converse is equally true: A strong sense of well-being is often the precursor to good health. It is difficult to feel terrific when you lack good health. Recovery from any state of poor physical or mental health requires putting together all the pieces of improved wellness: attitudinal, mental, and physical.

I can touch an individual who has a strong life force (sometimes called the *prana*, *Ki*, or *Chi* that flows through us) and actually perceive the electromagnetic charge flowing around and through him. Touching a person who suffers from chronic depression produces a different sensation. I have touched people whose bodies feel like suction vacuums. The energy depletion is so intense that the body draws energy from outside of itself, like a vortex. I need to keep my own body grounded and centered while working with such individuals. Professionals in this field occasionally suffer chronic exhaustion resulting from the energy imbalance between client and therapist. The therapist must be able to resist giving over her own strength, thus debilitating herself, to a needy client. She must have a lot of stamina and focus in order to manage her own energy simultaneous to working with an individual whose body can't seem to get enough. Ironically, a therapist who can take care of herself—not give anything away that is vital for her own health or energy—actually is working for the client's benefit. It is not in my client's best interest if I spend myself thoroughly during the session.

Doing body therapy with someone who knows how to relax, someone open to letting go, is delightful. It feels good to work closely with someone whose energy is so alive, because considerable pleasure is derived from a deep human-to- human energetic connection.

Let's look at Rex, whose body is energized and balanced. His joints are supple, his muscles and connective tissue fluid. Although Rex has a strong body, he has managed to avoid the tightness and stiffness often associated with bulky muscles. Psychologically, Rex has done a lot of work clearing and moving past old blocks and wounds; he has learned to focus on the present, the only time and place where his power lies. He has a loving marriage and has resolved most of the tough issues that many of us have with our immediate family members. Let's take Rex one step further. His relationships are warm and supportive, he is honest, he has high self-esteem, and his life works well by anyone's standards. Because he is in touch with his feelings, issues do come to the surface that need to be dealt with. Life may not be perfect for Rex, and it is certainly not stress free, but he is able to manage it effectively without compromise to his physical or psychological health. He is not stuck. Rex has a good handle on managing and releasing the pressures and contractions in his body and his mind. Rex's family, friends, and the people with whom he works enjoy his company. Although they may not be able to articulate it, they feel good in their own bodies when they are around Rex. He does not have a habitually defensive character, and he is strong and clear. He has an open heart and is energetically able to give and receive love.

THE ENERGY STORM

What happens to Rex when a crisis occurs? Let's imagine that Rex has just found out that his wife has a malignant tumor in her breast. In his body, Rex feels the powerful emotions of rage and grief. He is painfully aware of these emotions that move through him in waves. On some days, it seems to Rex that it is all he can do to feel his fear and sadness. His heart hurts. Anxiety stirs in his belly. Rex feels it all. He notices how uncomfortable it is to be so terribly sad. He feels more fear in his body than he has felt in years. Rex's experience is intense, profound, and agonizingly real. Some days he notices that he is moving with a much heavier body.

Rex doesn't resist what he feels. Ironically, this capability gives him precious moments when his process is not flaring up, when his body is relaxed and his heart pain free. Being in touch with himself consistently, he directly experiences this quiet time too. Because Rex has learned to tolerate the emotional intensity feeling his pain entails, and because he is fully capable of feeling his joy, he gracefully moves in and out of different energy states, depending on the feeling that needs to be felt at any time. Rex has learned to contain most feelings on the emotional spectrum, which, paradoxically, is how he lets his feelings go. (Those emotions that you feel but you resist feeling—those that you repress—are the ones that come back at a later time to be dealt with.) Having learned to live fully, Rex trusts himself enough to be present with his own feelings: He does not need to deny them or to "act" a certain way. This is exactly how Rex moves through and past the toughest blocks in his emotions and his energy. The pain, as part of his process, moves through him just as the joy does. Because he allows himself to feel, everything moves through him. Being able to express his love, his fears, and his anxieties to his wife enables Rex to take care of his emotional body. In light of this crisis, Rex is fortunate to know how to ask for and receive support from friends and family.

When an individual has done extensive work on himself, he gains a definite understanding of what it means to be centered and grounded. His body becomes the framework through which he processes the myriad of feelings that make up the human experience. When something threatens the pieces that compose Rex—the inner integrity and strength for which he has worked so diligently—he does not become permanently fragmented. He knows intuitively know how to bring himself back together after he has weathered the storm. He knows that this too shall pass. As painful as this experience is, he knows that what he feels is moving through him. Even though he is afraid, he knows this does not mean that he is stuck. *He trusts his process.* Although Rex is hurting, his emotional body is alive in spite of the wounds being inflicted upon it. Trust is an important element in Rex's ability to endure his pain. He trusts his ability to contain his pain: He trusts that even when he feels his feelings, they won't destroy him.

$$* \quad * \quad * \quad * \quad *$$

Working with people whose bodies are more difficult to work with can be equally satisfying. Often such individuals have great attitudes. A client who is eager and willing to explore his capacity to let go, despite personal challenges, makes my job more interesting. A rigid body is not the problem. A spirit of cooperation can make up for the lack of pliancy in the tissue.

The sessions I did with Jodi taught me a lot about the way energy moves and presents itself to be examined and handled. Jodi's history is interesting. I had Rolfed her husband before Jodi and I began our work together. Her husband had told me that his wife was the most terrific woman in the world. She was so supportive, so strong, such a wonderful wife. How did he get so lucky, he wondered out loud. What a happy wife he had, he said. He made quite a case for her talents, strengths, and good nature.

When I finally met Jodi, I was immediately struck by how *unhappy* she was. Was this the same woman described by her husband as being so "up" all the time? Her face was drawn. Her mouth looked like she hadn't smiled or laughed in a long time. Jodi had a number of nervous habits, including chewing the insides of her mouth and tearing the skin off her fingers. She suffered from Crohn's disease (inflammation of the intestines) and low self-esteem, and spent most of her time worrying about her husband and her three grown daughters. I quickly learned that Jodi took care of everyone but herself. She was a devoted and attentive wife, and her husband had completely missed the fact that she was terribly unhappy. She was so busy fulfilling everyone else's needs, that she herself desperately lacked the things she gave away energetically.

After a couple of months of working together, Jodi and I were doing a session that entailed her sitting comfortably in a chair, noticing her body, and staying present with her feelings. At first, Jodi, in her characteristic style, fidgeted and fussed: She was perpetual motion. All of her nerves appeared to be firing simultaneously. In an attempt to help Jodi unwind, I offered a few simple visualizations that helped her quiet her mind and nervous system. She breathed easier as the relaxation slowly entered her body. As Jodi sat quietly in the chair, she commented that she had never felt her body before. The look on her face was soft, yet she was concentrating. After several moments, as she gradually became more and more full of her feelings, many things about Jodi's body changed. She got warm and pink. Her hands lay soft and still in her lap. Her cheeks flushed and her jaw loosened visibly. Jodi's breath got deeper as she allowed it to emerge from lower down in her chest and belly. Watching Jodi's face was fascinating: I could see the storm moving in.

7
7

Jodi realized that her compulsive preoccupation with her family members was a way for her to avoid finally telling the truth about her own life, which was not fulfilling and had become empty. As she realized how she had given herself over to others, and how great the loss was, she sobbed. All of this occurred nonverbally; she shared her insights with me afterward. (Her only words during the process were, "This is the first time I can feel my Self.") By making contact with this quiet place inside her for the first time, Jodi became painfully aware of the wounds she had buried deep within herself. The pain she felt from having denied her own needs throughout the years were as real as those from a physical injury.

Jodi stayed relaxed and allowed herself to continue with the process, which took about one hour. She went through layers of self-discovery, including the grief of learning how she had not taken care of herself. She was sad to discover how empty she felt inside when she wasn't focused on the needs of others. Jodi was neither acting nor deliberating during this process. It had a life of its own, and Jodi allowed it to happen. She spent time going through these feelings, *as the feelings spent some time going through her.* Then, as the emotional storm began to blow over, Jodi returned to a deep relaxation; her body was softer and her mind was quieter. The feelings had run their course because Jodi allowed them to move through her. Jodi, like Rex, had survived the storm. The process came to an end, not because Jodi suppressed herself, but because there was a natural closure and completion. The feelings were finished being felt.

Having surrendered to it all, Jodi gained tremendous insight into her own being and how she had organized her life. In spite of the intensity and physical impact of the experience, the emotions and energy that moved through her did no damage. She reported later that it felt much better to feel sad than to feel nothing. It actually came as a tremendous relief to Jodi to feel the feelings that she had worked so hard to avoid all her life.

TRUE RELIEF

In the early days of Rolfing, more inherent value was ascribed to the big, cathartic events. I meet individuals who expect that they have to throw some kind of a fit during the therapy session in order to release the emotions that may be blocked in their structure. Others do throw a fit, but don't necessarily release anything. Often these people are simply expressing their frustration at remaining stuck. Their lives and bodies do not necessarily change as a result of this so-called release.

Now we know that the value of Rolfing lies not in the volatility of the experience itself, but in what is learned from the experience and how energy moves through the body differently with this newfound knowledge and insight. If no change occurs, then the histrionics have not been therapeutic in the true sense of the word. For some individuals, emoting doesn't release the energy, but rather recycles it. Real change is evidenced by a variety of noticeable events, such as the following:

1. *Increased physical relaxation.* The emotions stored in the body are often registered as tension in the musculature. As habitual and rigid forms of protecting and defending the Self are released, a person's body will feel softer. I call this "releasing the guard." Prior to this release of armor, the individual being touched may have felt pain, withdrawal, or hypersensitivity. In the later hours of Rolfing, there will be significantly less pain, more availability of the tissue, and more pleasure associated with being touched. In the case of yoga, doing the asanas gradually becomes less difficult, less uncomfortable, and, again, more pleasurable.

2. *Relief from chronic body armor.* A person will hold himself in fixed positions when the emotional body has been wounded or threatened. The individual trapped in a body with limited mobility has considerably

fewer options and less internal support. The tension itself prevents the person from feeling safe without the guard. It's rather cyclical. In such a case, self-expression is limited: A person with a body that is heavy and held down to the Earth has difficulty jumping for joy. As your physical body is loosened from its armor, you may move, play, dance, or make music spontaneously—impulses that had been thwarted by the chronic holding. Moving feels good when your body has been liberated to do so. You are also freer to experience and work with your emotional side, having made this information more available to yourself.

3. *The ability to respond in a new way to an old stimulus.* A person may stay stuck in his behavioral patterns because his body is caught in a groove. He has always gotten angry and depressed when his boss has given him constructive criticism about his job performance. The reactive button is physical and primed to be pushed. With the softening and loosening of the musculature experienced through Rolfing and yoga, however, he can imagine himself breathing and receiving the information without reacting to it, very unlike behavior from the past. He may stay present and relaxed in a situation that previously triggered a defensive reaction because Rolfing and yoga have taught him exactly how to do that. I have had clients over the years tell me that they have become better listeners since their body therapy. Physical relaxation enables a person to be more connected to present time and less reactive to events from the past.

4. *Relief from chronic health problems.* Stress, disease, and chronic visceral or muscular tension go together. Often people move away from disease and toward health as a result of their involvement in Rolfing and yoga. Jodi, for example, became completely free of any symptoms of irritable bowel syndrome after her fifth Rolfing hour. The chemicals, acids, and imbalance in her intestines had been a result of chronic anxiety and the physiological stress associated with it. Jodi began to change how she felt about herself. She learned to relax and was able to move into a state of greatly improved health.

5. *Significant weight loss or weight gain.* Many times the body carries excess weight or inadequate weight as an expression of some unresolved emotional trauma from the past. A woman who has never matured into the full psychological expression of her womanhood as a result of a series of molestations during her puberty, is an example. Because of her tremendous fear of her own sexuality and because her maturation was arrested at a critical point in her development, she became obese as a way of obscuring the sexual side of her being. In essence, she "desexualized" herself. If these issues become resolved through body-oriented therapy, perhaps with the additional help of psychotherapy, the woman may find herself approximating a weight more natural for her height and bone structure. Typically, her psychological state would improve as well.

   Other issues of weight show up in individuals whose bodies appear undernourished. Sometimes the individual is actually unable to take in nourishment, unable because of something that happened at an earlier time in his life. In an adult, the pattern manifests itself as an inability to maintain a normal and healthful amount of body fat. If this person learns to receive nourishment, indeed to nourish himself, his body may change to a more ideal size, perhaps one that is bigger, fuller, healthier, and stronger.

6. *The ability to contain a rich variety of emotions.* As was the case for Rex, if you are integrated and whole, you know intuitively that many emotions can move through your body. Here movement is the key; the feelings do not get stuck enroute. Being healthy and open does not mean that you will not feel the discomfort associated with a wide variety of emotional experiences. On the contrary, feeling all feelings, including discomfort, may be a measure of physical and psychological balance. Movement means flexibility, integration, and ultimately, equanimity.

7. *The sustained reduction of pain.* In many instances, pain has a nonmedical origin. Blood tests, X rays, CAT scans, exploratory surgery, and the like cannot explain it. Or even if the pain does have a medical origin, the psychological material attached to it prolongs it. One of my clients jokes

that I cured her brain damage. After a car accident eight years ago, she was convinced that she had brain damage. As the tension unwound, she discovered the payoff she got from the "brain damage" in terms of helplessness and never having to get on with her life. This woman's life has shifted 180 degrees since she released her attachment (the secondary gain) to the pain in her head.

Emotional release in general may enable a person in pain to move in a positive and healthful direction. Confronting your fear of moving (because of a painful back injury, for example) may enable you to release the pain. It sounds simple and often is.

Unexpressed anger can come out as pain or dysfunction. The work that is required to hold in these important feelings can have a negative effect on your physical and mental health. And although the inhibitory state may cause a problem on the one hand, it may provide a secondary gain, such as sympathy, revenge, or attention on the other. Or you may not know how to release the emotions but would be willing to do so if you could learn how.

Many years ago I had a client who was furious at her physician for having performed what turned out to be an unnecessary appendectomy. She had been unaware of her anger until she got Rolfed. The tenderness in her lower right abdomen had no medical explanation, but the anger that surfaced held a lot of meaning, as did the images and associations that she re-experienced from the surgery of some thirty-five years earlier. Resolving issues such as this one often releases the tension associated with the pain and frequently causes the symptom itself to disappear.

7

Chapter **SEVEN**

Holding Up and Holding Down

☙

Energetically and structurally speaking, there are two kinds of people in the world: those who lift their bodies up off the ground, whose musculature pattern is to pull up; and those whose muscles pull them down toward the ground, whose bodies feel heavy and are inclined to lose the battle with gravity. As with any oversimplified classification, some people display characteristics of both groups at different times and under different circumstances. As a body-oriented therapist and as a yoga instructor, I need to understand these groups in order to work effectively with individuals. To help produce positive changes that are pertinent to a person's unique way of making his body random and disorganized, I must make a careful assessment of his body style and holding patterns.

On a practical basis, the cues, instructions, and actual ministrations used with these two types differ. Many yoga asanas are tools for grounding the physical body. Individuals whose bodies are already heavily rooted—whose bodies are oriented downward, are, indeed, held down–obtain no therapeutic benefit from learning to "drop down into their bodies." They are already dropped into their bodies, and to a degree that has become a liability, not an asset.

Learning to do more of what you are already doing, in terms of holding, would not be a positive lesson, nor would it be a good use of time. If I do teach a person to amplify what he is already doing, I do so expressly to show him his pattern for his edification. I would not use such instructions for any other purpose. In other words, if I am going to guide a person deeper into his holding patterns or help him to become more aware of them, I must do so with utmost attention to his process.

A sensitive yoga teacher can detect a heaviness in a student's body. She is wise to offer asanas and visualizations that bring lightness and buoyancy. Instructions to "imagine five hundred helium balloons lifting the top of your head toward the sky" would work for such an individual. "Imagine your body as an oak tree growing roots deep into the Earth" would only drive this person deeper into his pattern. This second cue, however, would be excellent for the person with the opposite holding pattern, namely, forcing a lift throughout his entire body. Here is an example of the power of the teacher's words and the impact they have on the student. A suggestion made without consideration for the direction toward which this person moves when his body gets stuck could produce results that are antithetical to the objectives of yoga.

Similarly, a Rolfer is capable of affecting the way energy flows in the client's body. I touch my client's body with a certain directionality. This means that I am aware of how the energy gets stuck and in which direction I need to move my hands in order to address this. I often cue my client to allow his muscles to relax in the direction I am moving them with my hands. The direction is intentional and specific to the way the muscles contract in the context of the overall body pattern. For example, an individual who essentially holds his body up would have a different configuration in the muscular and fascial contraction in the legs than an individual whose body is chronically being pressed toward the floor. For someone whose pattern is to hold up in the legs, I would "speak" to the quadriceps with my hands in such a way as to address this fixation. When the quadriceps release, they drop down. For an individual whose legs bear down into the ground, release of this holding pattern may cause the quadriceps to float upward.

Functionally, holding your body up is a different series of behaviors than holding your body down. Another example is in shoulder tension. The scapula (shoulder blade) can be held up by the trapezius, which, when contracted, moves the shoulders toward the ear. (See figure 7.1.) Conversely, the scapula can be forced down toward the hip by the muscles that lay inferior to it on the back. (See figure 7.2.) When the shoulder relaxes in these two different scenarios, the body changes in two distinct ways. *Under these two* conditions, *different sets of moves produce the phenomenon we call relaxation.* It is the job of the Rolfer to educate the client as to just exactly how that relaxation takes place. What precisely do you do in order to produce that change? The extent to which the therapist personally and specifically addresses these patterns with each client determines the efficacy of the modality being employed.

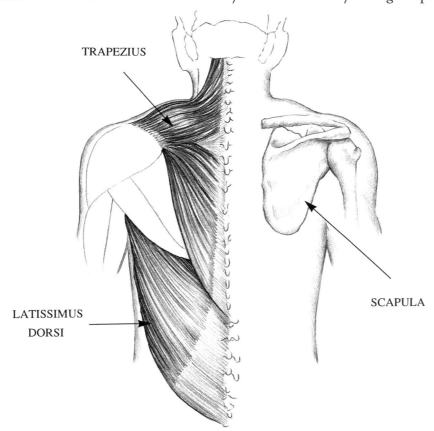

TRAPEZIUS

LATISSIMUS
DORSI

SCAPULA

Figure 7.1: The trapezius moves the shoulders toward the ear.

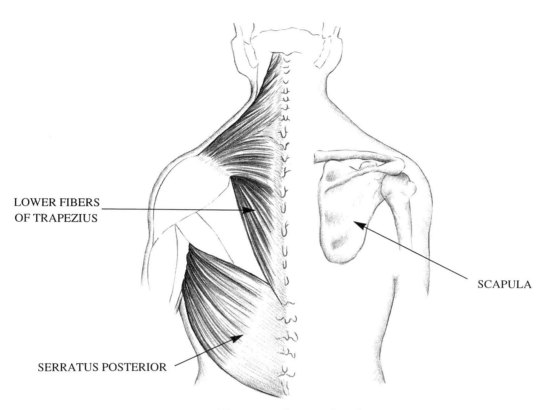

LOWER FIBERS
OF TRAPEZIUS

SCAPULA

SERRATUS POSTERIOR

Figure 7.2: The scapula can be forced down toward the hip by the muscles that lay inferior to it on the back.

Psychologists and psychotherapists with whom I have worked also find these classifications useful in dealing with clients. People who hold themselves up have a different character structure than those who hold themselves down. Let's look at this.

Marcy came in for Rolfing and yoga instruction several years ago. Marcy was a classic "holder upper." She had excelled in ballet as a child and had been instructed in the practice of lifting her ribs, her back, her head, and her feet off the ground. In ballet, this posturing comes in handy. It enables the ballerina to be light on her feet, to jump high, and to be easily lifted by her male partner. When the ballerina is not dancing, however, this lifting pattern becomes a problem in terms of the tension and blocked energy associated with it. Marcy had an "up" personality to go along with her body patterning. She was gregarious, outgoing, and success-oriented. She had a prestigious job at a radio station and loved being powerful.

A person's holding pattern is frequently congruent with the emotional posture he assumes in his life. It becomes the objective of the body therapist to work with these energy patterns and to establish balance and order within the context of the person's entire body. In many ways, Marcy's up patterns were an asset for her in terms of her professional achievements. Our work focused on the places where this pattern was an asset as well as on those where it was a liability. We were not interested in taking the pattern away, but rather in examining ways in which Marcy could make either gains or sacrifices in her life as a result of these holding patterns. We looked at the ways in which her "upness" left her with a lack of support in her legs and limited her options for expressing her true self in its myriad forms. Marcy knew it was hard work to be up all of the time, but she did not know how to give herself relief. She had internalized the pattern to the point that it had become a fixation.

Marcy complained of chronic fatigue and back pain. She also revealed to me how incapable she was of feeling her own "negative" emotions, such as sadness and fear, which she felt threatened her. Because these feelings were incongruent with Marcy's upness, her body did not allow her to cry. This is a problem when crying is precisely what a person needs.

Several sessions into her Rolfing, Marcy told me that she had made an amazing discovery that morning as she dressed. She had seen herself as she was dressing: She put on her underwear, she put on her shoes, she put on her clothing, *and then she put on her body.* Marcy actually felt herself assume a body stance as if it were her outermost layer of clothing, and something she needed before she could leave the house.

At first she didn't like what she saw. She got in touch with the fact that her outer garment was actually quite rigid and controlling. Being extroverted and gregarious was exciting, but Marcy had begun to feel the burden of having to maintain that expression throughout the day. She felt sad that she knew so little about letting go. I encouraged Marcy by telling her that the discovery of what she was doing in her body and how she was doing it was a giant step forward. If she could allow herself to sit with that piece of information, then she would probably move into deeper and deeper layers of herself and her body awareness.

People who hold themselves up are often living with an unarticulated fear and belief: If they don't hold it all together, they think they will lose themselves. This reminds me of a postcard I once saw many years ago:

> Don't ask me to relax.
> It's my tension that keeps me together.

This type of person gets his sense of self through the effort and force of lifting up and keeping it all together. Sooner or later, as happened with Marcy, this pattern becomes intolerable. Working with holder uppers is not easy. Many of them see themselves as invincible and deny the travail and exhaustion that is with them for most of the day. The challenge for these people is dealing with emotional and psychological information as they learn new ways of being in their bodies.

Marcy believed that her performance and success depended on her body posturing. It took about a month of Rolfing and movement work before Marcy felt safe enough to go into work with her back soft and relaxed, her front not pushed way out ahead of herself. For most holder uppers, the new reward—that is, the comfort in their bodies—becomes the incentive to consider changing the old pattern. Making genuine contact with people is much easier and more pleasurable when one has a soft, balanced, energetically available body. As these little windows of progress open up, a person becomes more willing to let go of the old holding patterns. I have yet to meet a holder upper who doesn't experience great relief once he finally gives himself permission to relax and let go.

People who hold themselves down, whose bodies are made heavy, require different work. In yoga, these individuals have a lot to learn from asanas that lengthen the torso and bring openness to the pelvis, diaphragm, and ribs. Yoga poses that convey a sense of lift and poses that bring the awareness overhead, moving upward, are ideal for "holder downers." These individuals get tremendous value from learning to allow more space in their bodies.

For a Rolfer working with a holder downer, it is important to instruct the client where "up" is. A holder downer often has his head chronically down and forward, another symptom of having succumbed to gravity. With the head forward and down, the person's viewpoint is oriented in the same direction. In this case, the individual's perception of his environment is congruent with the story being told in his body.

When I touch a holder downer, the touch should convey the possibility of energy moving upward. Or I can approach this person by enabling him to directly experience what he is already doing prior to introducing the idea of change. There may be great information in the pattern itself, and if so, this step is as valuable as letting go of the pattern. In either case, gradually learning to allow the head to rest on top of the neck can be powerful for holder downers. Sometimes a person looks out at the world from eye level for the first time that he can recall.

A holder downer with whom I am currently working discovered that allowing her head to rest on top of her neck enabled her to notice her environment for what seemed like the first time. She had never before noticed the beautiful colorful anatomy charts in my treatment room. Her perspective had been limited to the downward pull of her body and the mental energy required to sustain the heaviness of her head. This change in perspective can be the launching point for significant progress, as it was with this particular client.

People who hold themselves down are similar to those who hold themselves back. In this third pattern, the body seems glued to something behind itself, something that prevents it from moving ahead. The holding is often in the back muscles themselves (although the chest and belly can press toward the back, creating the same effect as "holding back"). By virtue of the holding in the connective and muscle tissue, if a person holds himself either back or down, then his spiritual, physical, and mental orientations will reflect the positioning of his body. Any movement forward is made more difficult because the body is moving against its own internal resistance. Going on a job interview, for example, is more difficult when the energy body is pulling itself way back, a move that is against the stated intention of the person's mind. People who hold themselves down or back are frequently underachievers. The chronic difficulty they face in making definite and positive movement in their lives baffles them. Accomplishing anything entails an extra burden, namely the weightiness of the body in its energetic holding pattern. When these people learn of their bodies' role in keeping them stuck, their awareness enables them to put something more positive in motion. Learning to allow their bodies to support the movement they wish to make in life brings about an important shift in their attitude and capabilities.

Claudia was a holder downer. Through Rolfing and yoga she got in touch with the internal pressure in her body that kept her in a state of nearly perpetual inertia. What was most significant to Claudia was not *that* she held herself down, but *how* she did. The way she pressed down into her pelvis cut off her sexual feelings. Although she wanted more aliveness and sensation in her body, she had tremendous difficulty feeling any sexual energy or even desire. She discovered how her body's holding patterns kept her from feeling energy in her pelvis as well as in her heart.

In his compelling book *Body, Self and Soul*, Jack Lee Rosenberg states

> Since pelvic blocks are reciprocally related to neck, throat, mouth, and shoulder blocks, freeing one area may be associated with increased blockage in the other. Therefore, we pay close attention to the upper body while opening the pelvis.[1]

For Claudia, the discovery of the bearing down tendency in her body had spiritual as well as physical implications. As a graduate candidate in transpersonal psychology, Claudia had a spiritual viewpoint, and she regarded the insights she gained through Rolfing and yoga as tools for developing and opening to her higher self. The release of the pressure in her physical body enabled Claudia to express aspects of herself that had been repressed by her body armor. This complemented the work she was doing both personally and in her education. Many individuals who are focused on their spiritual development discount their sexuality as being "unspiritual." This splitting off, or holding down, as in Claudia's case, actually compromises the self because a natural part of full expression is restrained. Claudia's body changed when the tension in her pelvis was released. And she had a direct experience of fuller expression of herself that no amount of intellectualizing or philosophizing could have equaled in helping her to become more spiritual, more actualized, more whole.

A fourth configuration is one in which the person holds himself forward. In this type of patterning, the person presses his body out in front of him. His head, his heart center, or his pelvis may be presented forward so as to throw off his center of gravity, thus keeping his body out of balance. This may be reflected by his psyche or his personality being out of equilibrium. A person whose body is prone to press forward may know only how to be assertive, how to put himself "out there" (literally), and how to move forward. Although these are certainly admirable personality traits, any one of them can become a liability and a threat to the ultimate expression of a person's full potential. At times a passive, receptive role is most appropriate. A body should allow a person variety in his expression of self and in his movement.

9
3

8

Chapter **EIGHT**

Levels of Holding

In the initial stages of my work with a client or student, I ask him what he has learned about his body throughout the years. I want to know what he has learned from his parents, teachers, physicians, religious leaders, and dance instructors, from the military, and through various professions, hobbies, and avocations. What has he learned to do to offset back pain, for example? What was he taught to do to correct his posture? In what ways does he hold his body to relieve pain, look more attractive, or appear more in control? Frequently people store in their bodies some sort of "teaching." Much of the time, I have observed, these teachings limit optimal functioning. As a general rule, a person cannot learn to hold his body correctly. Furthermore, these lessons often steer the individual away from being able to resolve the problems the instructions were intended to solve.

If you are seeking out Rolfing or yoga for relief of chronic pain and discomfort in your body, the lessons you learned prior to this time may not be working and may, in fact, be contributing to your problems. If you were taught to squeeze your buttocks to eliminate back pain (as was taught to one of my clients by another practitioner), and the back pain persists, something is wrong. Let's look at this in depth.

In 1986, I participated in a weekend seminar held in a large hotel conference room. A woman there had brought her own reclining chair, one of the light, portable garden varieties. I wondered why she had brought her own chair, so I asked her about it. She told me that she had a "bad back" and could not sit in the chairs provided by the hotel. She had grown dependent on her chaise lounge and took it everywhere. Throughout the weekend, I stole surreptitious glances at the woman, who lounged, while the rest of us sat in our nonergonomic metal folding chairs. I saw her walk around during food and bathroom breaks, and then return faithfully to her chaise lounge and gingerly lower herself into it.

The configuration of the woman's spine reminded me of a Slinky toy going down the steps. She had no strength in the muscles of her lower back, in the lumbar region. This was evidenced by the loss of length to her abdominal muscles, the posteriority of her lumbar vertebrae, and her tendency to remain doubled over even while standing. She was obviously in great discomfort and found standing to be extremely uncomfortable. Her back, I might add, was the approximate shape of the concave surface of the chaise lounge. (See figure 8.1.) The convexity of her back matched the concavity of the chair. Clearly, the lounge had not only failed to offer her support to change, but encouraged her deeper into her holding patterns. She was not recovering from the chronic pain and dysfunction in her back. *What she was doing to remedy her back was prolonging her problems.*

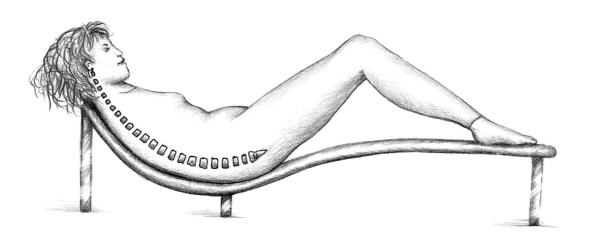

Figure 8.1: Chaise lounge with the spine following the contour of the chair.

During this weekend I began to understand the relationship between persistent, intentional behavior and the perpetuation of undesirable physical problems that the behavior is supposed to correct. I began putting together information on several different levels. In terms of holding patterns in the body, let's discuss the primary and secondary influences on the ways in which an individual can make his body rigid. Primary tension is unconscious, rather than deliberate. It occurs innocently and involuntarily, as a result of an occupational hazard, a habit (for example, holding a baby on one hip), unresolved problems resulting from illness or injury (such as compensatory glitches from a runner's knee injury), or other such influences. The tension appeared, and the individual suffering may have no idea where all of this holding has come from. Primary tension is often a physical reaction to mechanical stress.

Secondary tension results from learned behavior. The sources of this type of body armor are varied, but they are always conscious. For example, a well-intentioned albeit misguided parent may teach a daughter to shield her prominent breasts from boys, who might want to take advantage of her. The young teenager learns to collapse her chest and hide her breasts to protect herself. The structural complications that ensue in her adulthood are compensations that stem from this secondary, learned tension pattern. At first, the girl holds herself in a certain way on purpose, not realizing the harmful side effects of the tension. But the manner sticks and becomes habit, and the restrictions of holding are forced deeper into the structure. This story illustrates what Rolfers mean when we describe the layering effect of muscle and facial tension.

Here is an example of secondary tension. One of my clients, a woman named Abbey, told me that when she was a girl her mother had told her countless times, "Don't move your hips when you walk. Hold your weight up in your shoulders." It's easy to imagine what happened to Abbey's body when she followed her mother's instructions.

When Abbey became an adult, she learned that her mother was an incest survivor. Growing up in a household with a father and brother who sexually assaulted her, Abbey's mother had felt an enormous need to desexualize herself. She had used her own body to try to protect herself, to appear more powerful and unsexual, and to "face up" to the males in her family. That became her truth, and she projected it onto her daughter. As in this case, the source of secondary tension is typically a misguided and unidentified psychological aberration passed on from parent to child. In the same vein, many people believe that they have inherited their posture problems. In fact, young children often model their parents' postural distortions and develop similar problems as a result. The child may have "inherited" one or both parents' styles of guarding themselves.

As discussed briefly in an earlier chapter, health care professionals also often misguide their patients. In fact, the health care industry fosters many fallacies. A person who adopts a new behavior to help mitigate a health problem, often overlooks the fact that the behavior may be exacerbating the problem. Most back sufferers will follow the advice of a physical therapist or physician who teaches them to hold their abdominal muscles in to "protect" the lower back simply because the advice came from an authority. Frequently the patient fails even to realize that his back is no better. Clearly, he still hurts. But this person is unlikely to discover on his own that the learned behavior is not only not helping, but is actually perpetuating his problem. Ironically, he may wonder why his back isn't improving since he is following the instructions he received so diligently.

I see this phenomenon almost weekly in my practice. Often, when I ask my clients to show me the exercises they are doing to deal with the pain or

9
9

discomfort that brought them to Rolfing, they show me a set of exercises designed to mend the lower back. The sufferer is taught "crunches," any of a series of exercises in which he forces his body weight off the floor, doubling at the midsection in a sit-up fashion. Occasionally, this type of exercise might benefit a particular type of back injury, one that forces a concentration of muscle contraction in the abdominal muscles. Most types of back injuries and back pain, however, require lengthening and balancing of the front as well as the back of the body. Holding in the belly or overdeveloping the abdominal muscles to the point of hypertrophy compares poorly with a thorough, sensible, and appropriate plan to balance the front with the back in order to correct back problems. With the former scenario, secondary tension is overlaid on top of the primary tension.

All health care professionals should inquire of their patients or clients what they are doing to remedy their health problems. Learning how people believe they are supposed to live in their bodies can be illuminating. The root of many chronic problems lies in habits and behaviors that are a regular part of a person's way of life. Any attempt to change a person's habits and behaviors is bound to bump up against that person's belief system. Depending on the situation, this work can move quickly or arduously through the mental constructs that need to be dealt with. Clients often react defensively when I question something as precious and guarded as their beliefs.

A former client of mine named Carol once looked me straight in the eye and told me that she was *supposed* to squeeze her buttocks tightly to manage her back pain. Carol had experienced continual back pain for more than ten years. Knowing what she was doing in her body, I was able to use behavior modification to help her realize her goals in our work together. In order to recover from her back pain, she needed to relax her derriere and start moving her body differently.

It took several weeks before Carol was willing to consider a new idea: She was fiercely attached to what she had been taught and clung to her belief like a security blanket. My suggestions fell on deaf ears as long as Carol believed that she was "right" and my ideas were "wrong." I withdrew, allowing Carol to realize what she was doing with her body and remaining patient while she made the necessary discovery on her own. Considering that her habits might be perpetuating the pain was a big step, and Carol needed time to allow herself to take it.

Since her Rolfing more than five years ago, Carol has been pain-free. The final catalyst for this change was her own willingness to look honestly at what she believed about her body and then to entertain new ideas. For Carol, the release was as much a mental process as it was a physical one.

Another client, Anna, told me that her physician had told her never to release the arch in her back. She had learned this as a method for handling her chronic pain of twenty years. In my opinion, that's a long time to hurt. She had been following her physician's recommendation for ten years, despite the fact that her back pain had not abated. One of the main goals of our Rolfing and yoga work together was to enable Anna to move freely in her body, especially at her lumbar spine, without pain. I'll never forget how frightened she was even at the thought of softening her back. Her physician's words had been emblazoned upon her consciousness. The holding, as instructed by the physician, had become the secondary level of tension. Upon releasing it, we were able to find the primary tension, the original tension, which may have been caused by an old physical or psychological injury, and one that was relatively easy to work with. In Anna's body, the primary tension consisted of muscle tension in the hips and abdomen and associated structural limitations in the legs, pelvis, and back. The back arching was held over these older injuries. The success of my work with Anna was a function of working through the various levels of holding.

Sometimes you don't know how or why your body tightened in the first place. Sometimes this information presents itself in the form of an insight or a memory. Knowing why the body is tense is helpful for recovery and correction. But this information is not *required* for moving ahead into greater health and awareness. Insight into the past is like a gift. You can't plan on it, but when it occurs, it is quite special

DIAGNOSIS OR TREATMENT?

Rolfing is different from allopathic medicine in its approach to resolving health issues. I have gathered this information from my own heuristic studies, from watching my husband recover from a serious illness, and from listening to my clients and students throughout the years. Physicians want to find out what is wrong. While the physician searches for a label or a diagnosis, the patient himself may slip through the cracks in terms of getting the care he needs. In a similar manner, the standard of mental health was set by Freud, who developed his model of the mind from an intense study of people who were mentally ill. There is not yet a strong working model of optimal health in either the field of medicine or of psychology, although this is changing. Through his writing and teaching, Deepak Chopra, M.D., is making important contributions to the way people view their potential for optimal health.

> Your body is the river of life that sustains you, yet it does so humbly, without asking for recognition. If you sit and listen to it, you will find that a powerful intelligence dwells in and with you. It isn't an intelligence of words, but compared to the millions of years of wisdom woven into one cell, the knowledge of words doesn't seem so grand....You have to want to rejoin the flow of the body before you can learn from it, and that means you must be willing to open yourself to knowledge that was overlooked in your old way of seeing.[1]

Many patients are frustrated by the traditional medical model. The medical practitioner often spends a great amount of time attempting to find out what is wrong. In this process, the patient is frequently reduced to an organ, an isolated part of his body, or a physical entity void of spirit or emotion. The practitioner may ultimately determine an appropriate medical recourse, or she may simply waste the patient's time, energy, and money and cause him further suffering. This is not intended to slander the medical establishment in general, but rather to point out a common, definite problem that needs to be addressed. I meet people regularly who have spent thousands of dollars for medical help from a physician, only to end up with a diagnosis that they can't pronounce, much less understand. Patients need more than a diagnosis: They need personalized caring and healing.

Chronic pain is a classic example of a situation that sends doctors on a search. Many sufferers of back pain, chest pain, abdominal pain, headaches, and the like have nothing wrong with them in the medical sense, and thus doctors can't find anything. If the problem doesn't show up on X rays or an MRI, the patient is frequently dismissed and told that nothing is wrong with him. This is an ironic series of events: The patient suffers, but doesn't fit into a medical category, so the physician discounts the patient's subjective report of pain or dysfunction. In truth, the patient, in a case such as this, frequently needs something that the physician cannot administer in the first place. This attempt, then, to find out what is wrong can be a trap for the patient, often yielding only exorbitant costs and frustration.

Often, in Rolfing and yoga, we are not as concerned with learning what is *medically wrong* with the patient as we are with finding ways to help relieve the physical, emotional, and spiritual suffering of those seeking professional help in these areas. Many people whose pain clears up through Rolfing treatments and yoga stretches have the same conditions that led other patients to undergo invasive surgery or take high doses of medication. It's not that we

103

don't deal with technical, physical, and structural issues: In fact, we do that all the time. Often, however, we are able to proceed, simply with the information given to us by the clients, feeling our way as we go. The client's subjective report is often as valuable as the data generated by sophisticated medical diagnostic devices. In case this sounds unscientific, it is actually an excellent, intuitive, effective way to approach the body—and, yes, scientific, because we are dealing with laws, systems, and knowledge.

Recently, I taught a class in body therapy in which all of the participants happened to be women. One participant, Josie, explained that she hadn't been in class the previous week because of a severe headache. Josie said that she had suffered debilitating migraines since the third grade. She had been taking medication since she was a child, but the doctors could "find nothing wrong." The doctors said that they did not know what they were treating. Josie spoke about her headaches as a demon inside of her. She said she felt that the time was near for her to "crack the code" and finally figure out what had been locked inside of her for all these years.

We did a body therapy session in the class, with the support of the other participants. Through a series of breathing instructions, hands-on contact, and verbal cues, Josie finally relived the sexual abuse that had been perpetrated upon her by her grandfather. The way she held her body rigid on the mat, the way she forcefully shut down her breathing, and the way she contracted her head enabled her to understand the etiology of her awful headaches. This material had never before presented itself for Josie, even though she had been through years of psychotherapy and medical treatment. The "talk therapy" may have stimulated thoughts and feelings, but the physical touching was the final catalyst. Allowing these dreadful memories to resurface took courage, but Josie commented afterward that she felt as if her soul had been touched. We, in turn, were moved deeply by Josie's emotional work.

While I touched Josie's face during the process, I felt something very important under my hands. There were about ten minutes when she found it extremely difficult to feel what was going on in her body. Prior to the breakthrough of feelings and understanding, Josie resisted what her body was about to reveal to her. It was during this time, while my hands were on her face, that I felt an intense spasm in her zygomatic muscles, located in her cheeks. Suddenly I realized that the migraine headaches were directly related to the spasming of Josie's facial muscles, which was her way of blocking out the feelings. This pattern is unlikely to reveal itself in a medical exam, especially when the doctor does not touch the patient, which was so in Josie's case. And because Josie was unaware of what was going on in her face and head, she couldn't tell the doctor about the spasm.

When people learn that something is identifiably "wrong" with their bodies, the diagnosis itself can become a handicap. That is the pitfall of the medical model: Diagnosis often becomes a stumbling block for the patient whose wellness is in jeopardy. Granted, the doctor may deliver the bad news in a compassionate and supportive manner. But once a nonmedical problem, such as Josie's chronic headaches, gets treated in a medical fashion, the patient runs the risk of failing to pursue his own healing and recovery. It is difficult to climb out of the box in which the medical establishment often puts the patient.

This is why the doctors were unable to cure Josie of her terrible headaches. The very spirit inside her body needed to be healed. Unfortunately, no pill or placebo can fix a broken spirit. A condition such as migraine can sound so final. Furthermore, even when symptoms neatly match a diagnosis, the patient often feels more stuck once the pronouncement has been made, because he knows that he "has something wrong" with him. The real art is to combine medical and diagnostic technology with compassion and empowerment. There is nothing inherently incompatible about these different aspects of health care. Approaching a patient with compassion, an attitude that promotes healing of the whole person, and an understanding of the power of learning to relieve high levels of stress and tension can do wonders for the person who is suffering.

For Josie, learning what was wrong was not as valuable as learning what she was doing to continually recreate her suffering. When she discovered how she held her breath, locked her emotions inside, contracted her throat, and tightened the muscles of her face and cranium, she began to feel a bit more in control. When the patient goes from being a "victim" of the illness to feeling more in charge, the healing has begun from the inside—and that is the deepest level of healing possible, because that is where the injury and the holding are most damaging.

9

Congruent Movement

This chapter is intended to show, from the viewpoint of a movement-oriented therapist, how people accomplish changes through Rolfing and yoga. Movement work is the *functional* arm of Dr. Rolf's work. Through this process I am able to get involved with my client in regard to many of the unique and personal details of how he lives in his body, how he expresses himself physically, and how he, literally, moves through life. (Hands-on, manipulative work is the *structural* arm of Rolfing. This includes, for example, manual derotation of the femurs and lengthening of the erectors.) I can't expect my clients to integrate my work if I only work on their body with my hands. Education, essentially through movement work, is the means for bringing the changes and insights home to the client. Through movement work, the client learns the lessons in such a way that he is apt to take them with him out of the session.

A static body, lying horizontal on the table, reveals only a tiny fraction of the holding patterns and restrictions present in movement. With movement work, the limitations that need addressing present themselves. Ultimately, the benefit of the work is measured by how a person's body learns to move effectively. This is why movement work is called the functional aspect of Rolfing. A dentist might learn to relax his shoulders while resting on the Rolfing table. But if he couldn't implement this release while reaching over a patient's body, my work would be of limited value.

Many an individual struggles with living inside a body that prevents him from accomplishing many of the things he wants to do with his life. This includes people who are severely incapacitated, such as amputees, paraplegics, or quadriplegics. It also includes people living in relatively nondisabled bodies but handicapped in other ways. Imagine a man who desperately longs for a loving, committed relationship. If his arms are exceptionally tense and the energy is quite blocked around his chest (heart chakra), he may find it difficult to give and receive love in a way that satisfies his longings. If this man wishes to gesture toward his needs, his body may actually move in opposition to his desires. He may, for example, long to move toward the object of his love, but, unwittingly and uncontrollably, pull away.

When our imaginary man uses his voice to say things such as "I love you" or "Please hold me," the tension around his throat may prevent him from communicating effectively. The stammer and the catch in his voice are manifestations of blockage in the musculature. Your body, like the one of this imaginary man, may prevent you from getting your needs met. This is a significant impediment to optimal psychological health, the roots of which lie in the physical (structural) body.

Let's look at another example. Janet had been sexually frustrated for most of her adult life. She had seen physicians, psychiatrists, and psychotherapists in hopes that they could help her learn why her body didn't work sexually. Thirty years ago, she would have had the awful stigma of being diagnosed as *frigid*. Now this condition is called *preorgasmic*, which is less fatalistic than the old classification. Nothing was wrong with Janet's body from a medical point of view. *Functionally*, however, it did not support her in getting what she wanted in life.

Janet found it difficult to release her pelvis through Rolfing. The frustration she felt in her body while being Rolfed was similar to what she had felt when having sex. She did not respond, she was unable to relax (in the beginning), and she felt disconnected from any sensations in her body, especially in her pelvis. In the initial treatments, in response to cues designed to enable her to feel her body, she actually found it difficult to breathe. She became aware of the tremendous amount of tension in her body, but felt unable to do anything about it. The yoga stretches were equally challenging and difficult. Janet described her thighs as being rigid and cold like steel. Although she eventually learned to release the tension and indeed feel more of her body, stretching her pelvis was initially painful and uncomfortable.

Despite these hurdles, many positive things came out of the bodywork. For one, through Rolfing, Janet was able to finally confront the fact that her pelvis was so tight, so armored, that it would be impossible to tolerate a complete sexual charge in her body. This enabled her to finally deal with her problem, rather than simply talk about it. Janet had a direct experience of precisely what her physical body did to keep her from feeling pleasure and experiencing relaxation. Now, instead of having a problem that seemed to be happening to her, she experienced the problem from the perspective of having created it herself, and then recreating it over and over.

Talking about the tension in her past could possibly have loosened a small portion of the rigidity in Janet's body. Through talk therapy she had gained some valuable insights that helped to explain her history and the etiology of her condition. But as long as Janet's body *moved in the opposite direction* from the direction that would enable her to achieve sexual gratification, her psychological problems would remain unresolved and her physical frustrations would persist. Integrating the knowledge she gained from the body therapy was, ultimately, the key to allowing her movement, including important aspects of her sexuality, to be congruent with her desires and intentions.

* * * * *

If your body is depressed—that is, being held down in a compressed posture—you may have difficulty recovering from associated chronic or acute psychological depression until your body changes. Moving where you want to move in your life may be difficult if not impossible if your body moves in a different direction. Perhaps you long for more personal power and effectiveness. If your body has learned to shrink and contract in situations in which allowing for and expressing your power may yield important results, you may find it difficult to fulfill your potential. Ginny, a woman who came to me for Rolfing and movement work, complained from the beginning of her treatments that she felt like a scared, powerless mouse and that her life was going nowhere because of her ineffectualness. When I looked at her, I could easily imagine that I, too, would feel frightened, powerless, and plagued by a feeling of inadequacy if I were doing in my body what she was doing in hers. Ginny had a a round back, a sunken chest, and a suppressed respiratory system. Ginny felt frustrated that her life had not changed, despite all the verbal therapy she had been through. She complained of chronic exhaustion. I pointed out what hard work it was to live and move with the tensions that had accumulated in her body. Looking at her body, the fatigue she experienced was no mystery to me.

Learning to move differently finally enabled Ginny to gain some of the power she had never fully owned. She had been on a long search; she couldn't remember a time in her life when she had any energy to spare or anything other than extremely low self-esteem. Gradually, through our work together, her spine lengthened, her head found its way on the top of her body, and she was able to breathe fully in her chest for the first time. With these improvements in her body and her self-esteem, she commanded her life from a new position of power, determination, and control. This was tedious work, and the changes happened steadily, but gradually.

Effective leaders in all fields frequently integrate their bodies with their self-expression. Their movements are congruent with their intentions. This is, in part, how they create credible images. Currently Anthony Robbins, author of *Unlimited Power*, is a popular and charismatic leader in the field of success and personal achievement. Much of his strength and persuasiveness stem from his ability to move his body in a way that matches his words. People who train with him can feel, either consciously or subconsciously, the energy moving in his body. The high degree of congruency between Robbins's words and his actions makes him tremendously convincing to his audiences.

Throughout the years, many of my clients and yoga students have faced challenging dilemmas in their personal lives, ones in which they were dealing with chronic difficulties and repeated failures. Working together, we examined how their habitual patterns of movement were caught in ways that limited the full expression of their potential.

Several years ago Peter came to do some work with me. Peter was tall, large-boned, and heavyset. He had recently been transferred from Denver, Colorado, to Silicon Valley, California, to take a high-powered job as a top manager in an electronics company. Peter was responsible for mobilizing a large, weak department of the company into a group of top producers. One of his complaints was that he was exhausted from trying to move his management team toward achieving better results. This was the job for which he had been hired, but he was unhappy about how difficult it had turned out to be.

Peter told me that many of the people he was managing happened to be petite women. Having never learned to stand up to his full height, figuratively and literally, Peter had acquired the habit of lowering his body to approximate the height of the people with whom he interacted.

We recreated the work situation in which Peter was managing his team. He imagined that I was one of his delegates at work. Because I am small, Peter fell easily into the habit of lowering his body and shrinking himself to make contact with me. As he became aware of what he was doing with his body, he began to notice the physical strain that he endured constantly at work. Given the holding patterns and the concomitant energy drain he had in his body on a daily basis, it was no wonder that Peter had great difficulty creating a genuine winning situation for himself and the people with whom he worked.

Peter told me that he was afraid of intimidating people by his size. In our working together, he said he could feel how he used his energy to get under me and try to push me up to a higher level of performance. This was the same thing he did at work. He said he actually felt the need to "come down to my level" in order for me to trust him. The body position he used to achieve this was uncomfortable and tiring and required considerable muscular tension. Peter wanted to inspire his team. Instead, he was modeling a fairly submissive, obsequious type of character.

Gradually Peter learned to stand up to his natural six-foot-two in height. These changes came as a result of the Rolfing, stretching and movement work we did. He began to see the people in his life much differently from this vantage point. We worked with various visualizations until Peter was able to see and feel himself inviting people up to connect with him. As he changed his movement patterns so that they were more congruent with his intentions, he became more effective naturally, without the exhaustion and frustration that had typified his work experience previously. And with his body open and his breath more vital and full, people felt differently around him, inspired by his grandeur. Ultimately, the performance of the employees in his department improved, as the frustration and fatigue on Peter's part lessened.

Movement education is not a panacea. But, chronic frustration may be more related to the shape and holding of the muscle and connective tissue than you realize. Getting your body in a position, both literally and figuratively, in which your movements are congruent with your highest desires will make a noticeable difference. And the changes that result from this kind of work are substantial enough to validate the time and energy you will expend to get your body to support what you do and who you are.

113

10

Chapter TEN

The Inner Angle

🙋

This chapter and the next will appeal to those interested in some of the technical aspects of Rolfing and yoga. Although it would be impossible to teach either one strictly through a book, two concepts are so fundamental to both disciplines I wanted to include one here and one in chapter 11. The Inner Angle is the basis for approaching restrictions in the muscle tissue through manipulations as well as through stretching. I gained an even greater appreciation for the effectiveness of this method when I applied it in my work with my Rolfing and yoga students. This material, along with the discussion of tadasana and the Rolfing line in chapter 11, will allow you to see deeper into the mechanics of Rolfing and yoga, and to see on yet another level why the two are so compatible.

Let's use the following working definition of the *Inner Angle*.

The Inner Angle is the muscle, or muscle groups, and their tendinous attachments that would perform a particular kinesthetic movement (such as the hamstrings bending the knee, or the biceps flexing the arm), but that are asked to soften and yield to the support of gravity, or to the practitioner's hands, while the movement is performed passively, without their help.

The Inner Angle is named for the inside of the joint space, the area anatomically opposite the area being stretched. Visually and functionally, this is the inside of the angle, where the movement occurs. If the knee is brought to the chest, for example, the Inner Angle is deep in the front of the hip joint. (See figure 10.1.) If the client can release here, if he can allow this movement to occur while his body remains passive, he has learned the valuable lessons that working the Inner Angle can teach. I usually put my fingers deep into the Inner Angle to make sure that the tendons that cross here at the joint haven't shortened. When I do this, the client becomes more aware of this part of his body, more in control, and thus more able to relax and release.

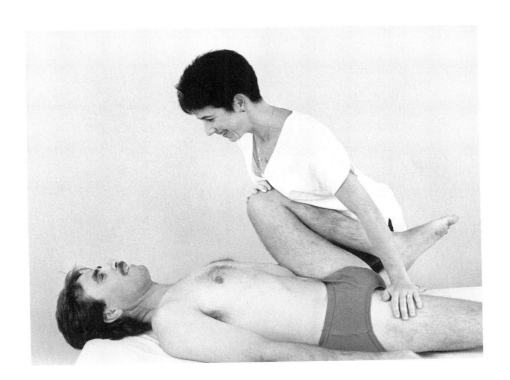

Figure 10.1: When the knee is brought to the chest, the Inner Angle is deep in the front of the hip joint.

The Inner Angle includes parasitic muscle groups. These groups are made up of contracted muscle fibers whose kinesthetic activity performs no useful function in the expression or movement of the body. For example, if you are sitting in your seat, the habitual lift upward of your trapezius muscles serves no purpose other than to confuse and fatigue your body, and perhaps to distract your mind. Your intention is to sit down. If your body is unwittingly holding up, than your movement is not congruent with your intention. (See chapter 9.) The chronic contraction of the parasitic muscle groups inevitably limits the flexibility in your entire body, including areas that have no obvious functional connection with the parasitic groups.

This concept is central to the effective blending of yoga and Rolfing. In yoga, an understanding of the Inner Angle is a powerful tool for being able to effectively release tension that inhibits flexibility and joint mobility. It also crystallizes Dr. Rolf's concept of lengthening while moving, which is her ground-breaking interpretation of functional biomechanics and kinesiology. Conventional wisdom says that bones move at the joint, and that the muscles, which cross the joint and whose job it is to make that move, contract. Dr. Rolf taught that when our bodies are organized and integrated, and when we move efficiently with the support of gravity, our muscles lengthen when we move. This single concept in Rolfing revolutionized the worlds of body and movement therapy. It also blended perfectly with my yoga practice and research.

Imagine that I am sitting at the head of the table, doing neck work on my client. The client's head is turned to the right. I am working on the left side of his neck, below the left ear, and around the left clavicle. But the head seems a little stuck. It is easy to feel the reluctance of the head and neck to rotate to the right. (See figure 10.2.) I feel as though I am working against an impasse. As I gently push against the head to further rotate it, something pushes back at me. The push comes from the Inner Angle, in which the tendons are unable to yield passively to this movement. It is not a true resistance to the stretch that I feel, in terms of a lack of flexibility or stretch-ability. Instead, my client is *unable to allow* his head to be turned. He is unable to let me move his neck, without "helping."

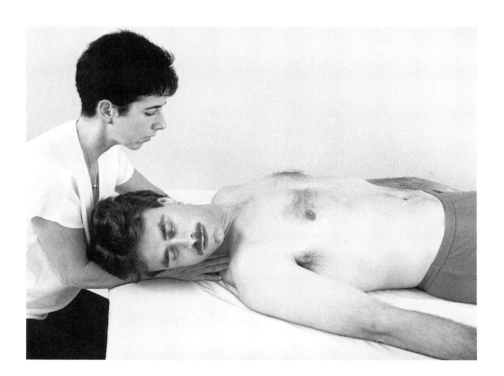

Figure 10.2: With the client's head turned to the right, it is easy to feel the resistance, the reluctance of the head and neck to rotate to the right.

On the right side of the neck are the muscles whose function it is to rotate the head *to the left*. (See figure 10.3.) The head won't rotate this way, because the muscles that would normally perform this function are short and rigid. This rigidity prevents the muscle group from softening. *It is also key in preventing flexibility in the antagonist group.* This is the Inner Angle.

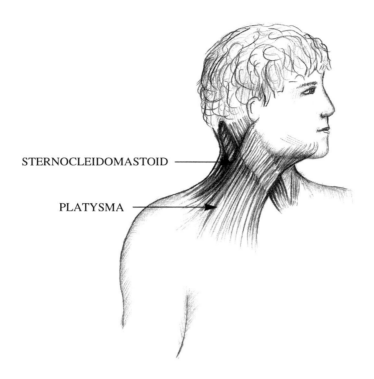

STERNOCLEIDOMASTOID

PLATYSMA

Figure 10.3: On the right side of the neck are the muscles whose function it is to rotate the head *to the left*.

For the head to rotate to the left *passively*, these muscles need to soften and fold like an accordion. If the muscles do not let go, the client's head and neck cannot give in response to my manipulations. The client reports this kind of problem as a limited range of motion. Inflexibility is not only the result of muscles, or muscle groups, being unable to lengthen. It is also the result of antagonist muscles being fixed and unable to release. Trying to move under this condition is like attempting to close a door that has a doorjamb in it. This principle applies to the entire body.

Working the antagonist group, asking the muscles that normally *would* perform this particular function to let go into my hands, is extremely effective in increasing the range of motion. The aspect of Dr. Rolf's work that focused on lengthening while moving really makes sense to me in this regard. She taught that the tendons and muscle groups on the inside of the angle of movement need to yield and release. Rolfers, by virtue of our training, have the skills to produce these changes with our hands. By supporting the client's body in a number of different movements, I figure out what is being stretched and what is being asked to fold and soften while the client surrenders the movement to me. I teach the client to copy this new and efficient way of moving by pointing out the movement alternatives as he lets go in my hands.

HEAVY AND LIGHT

While manipulating the client's body, I look for some specific indications that the results I am working toward are indeed occurring. My objective is for the client to feel safe enough to allow his body to relinquish some of the guardedness in the soft tissue (or to clearly and directly experience precisely how he guards himself and what feelings are associated with doing so). Any part of his body that I move may respond to the particular and deliberate support that I offer. If I move his arm, for example, I want to feel the natural weight of this particular limb. However much this arm weighs, I want to hold and support precisely that amount. His arm is heavy. He lets his arm go, in my attentive, willing, and able hands. *He does not "help." His body is at rest. This is his natural weight. His arm is heavy.* I can feel the heaviness and the associated release that occurs. And although his arm is heavy, it is relatively easy to manipulate, because it does not resist the movements.

I move the arm around slowly enough that the client has time to notice any tiny patches of holding. By virtue of the support I offer, he may feel spontaneously moved to release the resistance in his body in general, and in his arm in particular. Thus his arm becomes light. The lightness becomes the result of moving in a spectrum now virtually free of internal resistance. His arm does not push against or pull away from me. It is light. *He does not press against or pull away from the support I am able to provide. His body is at rest. This is his natural weight. His arm is light.*

At this point it becomes obvious that I am looking for a feeling that is both heavy *and* light. Because the work of a body therapist, especially a Rolfer, is so focused on the body's relationship to the gravitational field, this concept is imperative to our understanding of the human structure. When my body allows gravity to support me, when I am connected to the ground I stand on, my body is at rest. I neither push against the ground, thus making my body heavier, nor lift myself up and farther from gravity's ubiquitous influence. In the latter case, I would be creating a contrived lightness in my body. I say *contrived* because of the enormous work load associated with holding my body up—or in any direction, for that matter. My ability to feel my natural body weight is the true measure of my ability to be supported within the gravitational field. The feeling associated with this is restfulness and surrender. A feeling of peacefulness results from being so utterly connected to and supported by my physical environment. I often feel an inner glow when I let my body go to this extent. I am not working, which comes as a great relief. We are discussing a *state of being.*

When you begin to live with considerably less internal resistance in your body, your perception of your environment and the individuals with whom you live and interact alters. As you release the various ways you have learned to stiffen your body, you feel a greater connectedness with the people around you. I always imagine universal love to be a feeling that arises when the physical body, including the musculature around the heart, has opened beyond former habitual restrictions. Love is not just something you think about: It is a powerful emotion that is grounded in your body. And what better way to feel this emotion than to eliminate internal resistance, thus opening yourself to the greatest love of all, love of the Self? When I contemplate God, love, or any spiritual force greater than myself, I see this as an expansion, an opening. I gain access to this connection through the deep relaxation of my physical body. This can occur only with the quieting of my mind, the other part of expanding from the inside.

Yoga and Movement Work

I experienced the *aha!* of the Inner Angle and lengthening while moving in my yoga practice, and while leading groups and individuals in yoga. Ironically, this principle was fundamental to my yoga work already in progress. Through my study of Rolfing, I acquired new words to describe something I had already known. In any yoga asana, particularly the ones that require flexibility (versus the ones that focus primarily on balance or strength), several events occur in your body simultaneously. A simple forward bend is a good example. The entire back side of the body is stretched. From the calcaneus (heel) to the occiput (base of the skull), the demand on the body to let go can be quite high, depending on your flexibility.

The ultimate release across the back side is facilitated by a corresponding softening on the front side. *If the front of the body tightens, the back side shortens.* (See figure 10.4.) For example, if the hip flexors (front side) are tight, the hamstrings (back side) are inhibited. The spanning across and deep into the hip joints in flexion is a by-product of the lengthening of the muscles and tendons *surrounding the joint*. Unless all muscles (or muscle groups) and their respective tendinous attachments lengthen in movement, the integrity of the entire joint is compromised.

Figure 10.4: If the front of the body tightens, the back side shortens.

Muscles and their tendons contract in the course of any movement sequence. The biceps must contract to produce the strength necessary to lift a ten-pound weight. Yoga and Rolfing offer a reevaluation of the countless ways our bodies have gotten into the habit of contracting. Dr. Rolf called these movement patterns random. A body that moves with internal pulls and shortness is disorganized. When we bend over to tie our shoes, for example, we don't *have to* contract the muscles of our hip joints. Gravity could very well guide us downward.

To see this more exactly, disregard the notion that the front and back of the body are two separate entities. *The body is separated only when the layering of tension disturbs the integration.* When the movement and the release come from the *inside*, there is no separation, and the movement and release drop down into the core level. This is, ultimately, how a well-integrated body functions. In working with Rolfing clients and yoga students, it is extremely satisfying to witness the release from this deep place. It looks like a wave, an opening that happens someplace deep between the front and back sides. I often have the sense that this is the place where fundamental change occurs. Loosening an Achilles tendon usually will not affect your life greatly. But when this release moves into your leg, when your nervous system adjusts to accommodate the increase in energy and flexibility, the work becomes powerful indeed. These deep releases tend to spread throughout your body.

In yoga, it is easy to feel that contracting the front of your hip joints, particularly where the quadriceps originate above the hip joints themselves, causes the back of your body to tighten. The harder you work, the more your body rebels by pulling back. As a Rolfer, if I am doing a manipulation in which I bring the client's knee toward the chest and I encounter some stiffness across the back, I can effect a release by applying pressure to the lower, lateral portions of the abdomen, deep into the hip flexors across the hip joints. This is the Inner Angle. It is an invaluable tool for me as a Rolfer and an excellent application of the principles of yoga. In this case, the release goes through the front directly into the back. The back and front are no longer separated by tension in the muscle and connective tissue.

1
2
5

DEVELOPING STRENGTH

Muscles lose their strength when the resting length of the fibers has shortened past a critical point. The muscle fibers fatigue. Chemical waste products of the chronic contraction build up and irritate the nerves. Releasing tension actually increases strength. The muscle is rejuvenated from the fresh flow of oxygen and other nutrients carried to it by the blood. I always promise my body-building clients that the relaxation will not debilitate them. Invariably, they confirm this experientially.

There is another aspect to this. Imagine the muscles acting as a series of pulleys and levers. As your arm lifts overhead, the trapezius and deltoids come into action. The muscles that are being stretched are under the arm (triceps) and alongside and in back of the torso (serratus anterior and latissimus dorsi). (See figure 10.5.) If the connective tissue being stretched has foreshortened as a result of chronic or acute tension, the levers lift against a counterforce. This significantly increases the drag against the limb being lifted (in this case, the arm). Subjectively, your body records this experience as weakness in the arm and shoulder. Exhaustion sets in after you engage in physical exertion and tension-provoking activities. In this scenario, your body works in a field of internal resistance. It pulls against itself.

Weakness in the body is a complaint I hear frequently from my Rolfing clients and yoga students, and one that motivates them to seek the work. Currently I am working with a woman who went to a neurologist for weakness in her right arm. He operated on her neck, replacing the disk between her fifth and sixth cervical vertebrae with a bone chip from a cadaver. The weakness in her arm did not go away. Only through stretching and Rolfing manipulations did her underarm and the sides of her torso release extremely deep and knotty tension. With these treatments, the weakness in her arm disappeared promptly. Without the resistance, she achieved a complete, strong, and easy range of motion in her arm and entire shoulder joint. Depending on the nature of the problem, sometimes yoga and Rolfing provide a simple correction for a troubling condition.

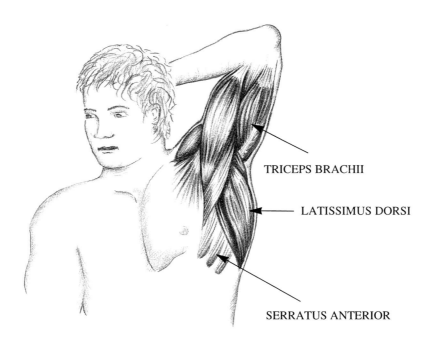

TRICEPS BRACHII

LATISSIMUS DORSI

SERRATUS ANTERIOR

Figure 10.5: As your arm lifts overhead, the muscles that are being stretched are under the arm (triceps), and alongside and back of the torso (serratus anterior and latissimus dorsi.)

CREATING A HIGH DEMAND

Another application of yoga to manipulative therapy comes as a result of the demand placed on the body in a variety of positions and stretches. Rolfers use the Z position to ask the pelvis, hip joints, and spine to lengthen and move in a particular way. (See figure 10.6.) Like any yoga asana, the Z position places a unique demand on the body's flexibility. I work on the client in the Z, asking him to move while I manually loosen and soften the areas of restriction. The Z position is effective for mobilizing the hip joints and lengthening and balancing the legs. The client sits in the position first facing one side, and then the other. I often get quite a bit of information about how he moves, or is unable to move, in response to this particular demand. Where does he get "hung up"? Where are the disruptions in terms of the fluidity and flexibility throughout the entire fascial web? How and where is the body holding back? What happens in his spine? What doesn't give?

Why not use other stretches to help me get even more information about a client's body?

In fact, I do. The Z position is not sacred in terms of addressing all of the imaginable tightness and areas of inflexibility in a given body. Only through a wide range of stretches can the entire picture come into focus. For some individuals, the Z position is easy and I get little information. There is no visible disturbance to the lengthening of the entire network of connective tissue, the sacrum rocks effortlessly, and everything seems to lengthen.

If not much happens in the Z position, it is appropriate for the Rolfer to modify the leg position to see if the deep release is maintained. Can the client's body stay relaxed in response to a *different* demand, or does it pull up, or back, or away? Herein lies the beauty of using a variety of positions to challenge the body. Ultimately, the greatest potential for movement, flexibility, and range of motion comes not from one or even a handful of stretches. The wider range of stretches asks more of the body in terms of releasing chronic tension on a deeper level. If one stretch doesn't get to a particular fixation in the musculature or connective tissue, another one will.

Figure 10.6: Rolfers use the Z position to ask the pelvis, hip joints, and spine to lengthen and move in a particular way.

Figures 10.7 through 10.11 depict the Rolfer working with the client in a variety of stretches. This is a random sampling, not an exhaustive list. There are countless creative ways to stretch our bodies. My goal as a Rolfer is to lengthen the connective and muscle tissue in my client's body; it makes perfect sense, therefore, for me to implement the wisdom of yoga to pre-stretch the various parts. If the client's body is prone or supine on the table, I can stretch him in a variety of ways. Even more options are open to me if I have him move, or if I move him, in various opposing directions. The Inner Angle comes to life only when the body is in movement. This is true for so much of the information contained in the body. When we lie still, we do not reveal the secrets of our bodies: These become evident only when we move. How we move then, is how we live.

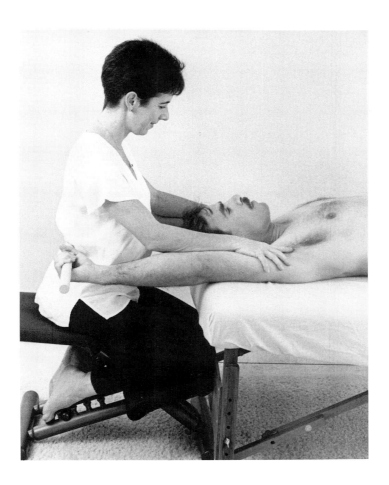

Figure 10.7: Figures 10.7 through 10.11 depict the Rolfer working with the client in a variety of stretches.

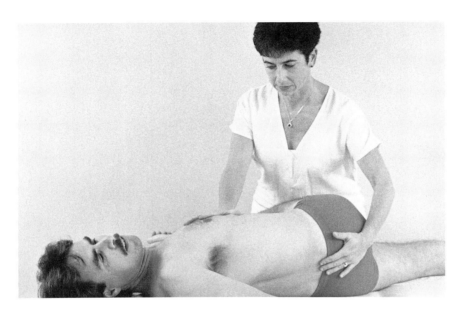

Figure 10.8:

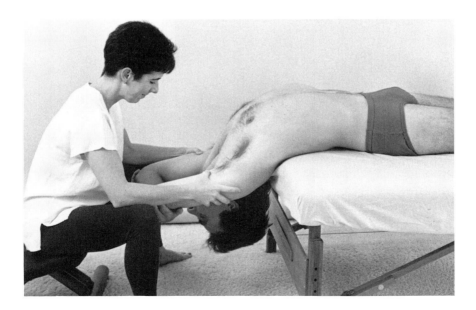

Figure 10.9:

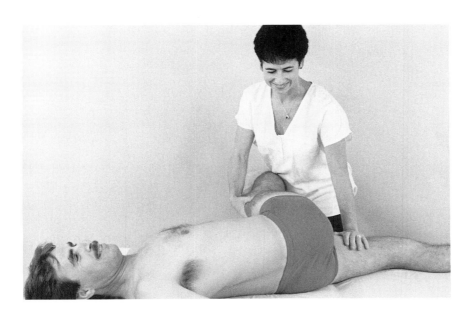

Figure 10.10:

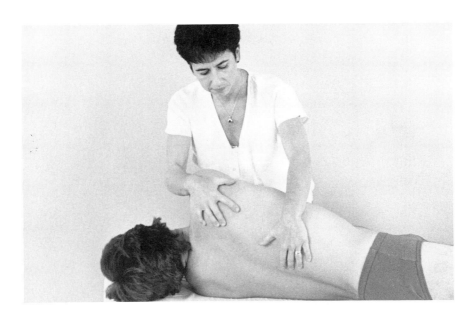

Figure 10.11:

11

Chapter ELEVEN

Tadasana and the Line

The basic standing yoga asana is called *tadasana*. Translated, this means "the mountain pose." The beauty of the mountain pose is that the body is neither held down nor held up. In fact, it is not *held* at all. Yet, paradoxically, the body *is* both up and down. The "down" is the energy that the openness in the pelvis generates and the aliveness that is sent to the legs and feet. The body is truly at rest on the floor, unlike the body of the "holder downer," which pushes down against the earth and is stuck there from habituation. In tadasana, the body is also alive with energy that moves toward the heavens with the lightness and effortlessness that come from space within the structure. The body is organized around an imaginary line that seems to be spiraling upward without any effort on the part of the body. As you will see, this *Line* is part of the basic premise of Rolfing and Rolf Movement Integration.

Energetically, the body is light and alive. Unlike the body of the "holder upper," it enjoys the naturalness of being up, without the effort of holding this position with muscle tension. This body contains pleasure, vitality, strength, and balance. Like the mountain, it is connected to the earth at its base, and the top soars toward the heavens and God. A human body supported from both directions knows no limitations. Energetic connection with the heavens allows the full spiritual and physical potential of the human being to be realized.

Both the holder downer and holder upper find aspects of tadasana that are personal and meaningful. Only in relationship to gravity and to the space around your body can you learn to let go deep in your structure. Holding up and holding down are two ends of a continuum, two extremes. Regardless of where you are along this continuum, regardless of how you hold your body, you must discover precisely what you do when you allow your body to move toward balance and integration. Just as making your body rigid disturbs the psyche, there is tremendous liberation, spiritually and psychologically, as well as physically, when your body becomes free.

Learning the mountain pose can resolve many of the conflicting energy patterns that cause structural problems in the body. In the mountain pose, the feet are placed on the floor approximately hip distance apart, just the right distance for the legs and feet to be under and in line with the pelvis. The femurs (thigh bones) are at a slight diagonal from the hip to the knee. With the feet positioned in line with the hips, the feet are in the ideal position to support the pelvis. The feet are open and soft on the floor, neither gripping nor pulling up. The lower leg bones are balanced slightly in front of the calcaneus (heel bones) and move vertically relative to the floor. The muscles and bones of the legs and hips are aligned appropriately. This enables the feet to stabilize over the arches, a position that provides as much support for rest, as well as for movement. The knees are loose, yet balanced and strong, offering precisely the right amount of stability to the thigh bones. The knees are neither bent nor hyperextended. Only in the natural extension of the knees are the quadriceps and hamstrings able to relax equally while the individual stands. The pelvis floats on top of the legs. (See figure 11.1.)

Moving up from the knees, the thighs and hips are soft, the muscles having tonus even in the relaxed position. The femurs are positioned in the centers of the thighs, rather than being pushed toward the backs or the fronts of the thighs as a result of the weight being off the natural center of gravity. The pelvis contains a lot of energy in the mountain pose. There is a suppleness in the pelvic floor, also called the perineum, and also a resiliency, because of the potential strength of the muscles in the perineum. The aliveness and openness in the area around the genitals further allow energy to move from the body, through the legs, and into the feet. The word *streaming* is often used to describe this energetic current in the body.

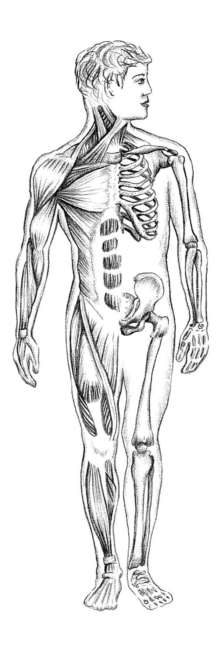

Figure 11.1: Full figure of aligned skeleton.

The belly and lower back reflect the balance and alignment of each other in the mountain pose. The belly is the front of the back, and the back is the back of the belly. Functionally, in terms of movement, the belly and back are not separate. In the mountain pose, the comfort and ease around the entire torso, lower and upper, front and back, reveal the energy that flows here. Standing vertically requires surprisingly little muscular tension. The body achieves its verticalness from the relative balance, strength, and suppleness in the front, back, and sides of the entire body, and from the relationship between the inside of the body at the level of the intrinsic muscles and the larger, superficial, extrinsic muscles.

The mountain pose is not a function of *holding yourself* vertically. Rather it is a function of *allowing yourself* to be vertical. You do not hold yourself up. You let go of the tension that pulls you down. Likewise, in tadasana, you do not hold yourself down. You let go of holding yourself up. The notion of "holding correct posture" is oxymoronic.

In tadasana, the area around the heart is alive. When the diaphragm lets go, the heart center has the necessary support from underneath and is allowed to expand. Students learning tadasana often feel energy moving into various body parts of which they had been previously unaware. When the chest is allowed to open and the breath finally moves into the musculature around the heart, people often feel exhilarated as this part of the body is enlivened. The heart center in chakra terminology is the seat of our deepest emotions. Many of these emotions get stirred up when this part of the body gets opened for the first time. Frequently in tadasana, students will display a release in autonomic nervous system function. Skin tone and breathing patterns improve. A deep feeling of relief comes from the relaxation and the integration of the various parts of the body with one another.

1
3
9

The back muscles are at rest because the body is in balance. Like a tent that is supported equally by each of its tent poles, the body gets its length and alignment from the internal structures, not from tautness and tightness on the outside. (See figure 11.2.) The body in tadasana is at rest. The person in this state experiences profound aliveness and alertness; coupled with the quietness of the mind, tadasana can be deeply meditative. The shoulders sit comfortably on the ribs, with space between the scapulae and softness in the trapezius muscles. The breath moves equally into the upper back and the chest. The upper body opens laterally, as well as front to back. In tadasana, the front is not forced open at the expense of the back, nor vice versa. The body is balanced.

Figure 11.2: A tent is supported equally by each of its poles.

The head rests comfortably on top of the body in the mountain pose. The connection between the head and the shoulders is the neck. The relaxation and proper alignment of the neck muscles enable the head to float at the top of the body. It simply rests there, by virtue of all of the underlying structures being balanced and supportive. The neck muscles are relaxed. With the weight of the body balanced comfortably through the center line, there is no pull of the head to move forward or be held back. The head is light in tadasana.

The position of the arms is consistent with the comfort and ease in the rest of the body. The arms and hands hang softly in line with the midline of the body, that is, they are held neither forward nor backward. When the chest and upper back are mutually balanced, the connection between the arms and shoulders is effortless and natural. Energetically, the arms are giving and receiving, capable of both but locked into neither. The jaw hangs gently, as there is room in all of the major hinges of the body. The eyes are soft, gazing out levelly. The ability to perceive and be attuned to the external environment, blends perfectly with the quiet and pervasive body awareness that comes from within. Tadasana is pleasurable. It is the epitome of balance and relaxed concentration. As one of my students so aptly stated, in tadasana, you relax as hard as you can.

THE LINE

Rolfers work with a principle called the *Line*. This is an imaginary flow of energy in the centermost position of the body, around which the entire body organizes itself vertically. The Line is alive in the mountain pose. It is the metaphysical column of vitality that supports the openness of the physical body. To some, the Line is a thought, a mental construct that describes the body when it is properly and comfortably aligned. To others, it is the experience of expansion and aliveness organized by the spatial relationship of the joints and fascia in the human structure. As a Rolfer and as a yoga instructor, I see the Line as the basis of the mountain pose. Mastery of the mountain pose is the precursor for balance, grace, flexibility and fluidity in all of the other yoga asanas. Likewise, the Line, as we refer to it in Rolfing, heralds movement within the broadest scope possible of the human potential. A person moves around his Line. He finds his Line in order to find his center.

Part

Two

12

Chapter TWELVE

Getting Started with Yoga

The asanas presented in this part are designed to enhance and reinforce the results obtained through Rolfing and Rolf Movement Integration. Continuing your studies with a teacher in your geographical area is invaluable. The trained eye of a yoga instructor can help you to correct your poses and avoid perpetuating poor postural habits when you stretch. An instructor who sees your body in movement and from a structural point of view can also advise you regarding how and why certain poses may be contraindicated for your body.

One of the advantages to private yoga instruction versus a group class is that you receive individualized attention. When working with a group of twenty students, the yoga instructor inevitably deals with a variety of structural patterns and problems. What one individual needs in the mountain pose may be entirely different from what someone else needs. Each person releases and lengthens a different group of tight muscles to move from chronic holding in his body to alignment and suppleness. An experienced yoga instructor recognizes this and tailors the instructions accordingly. In a large class, ideally you will see the instructor offer alternative postures to students for whom the posture being presented is contraindicated. You should expect that the teacher would give you personalized attention if any of the asanas appear to cause you significant pain or discomfort. Finding a competent instructor is well worth your time and energy and will help ensure your success in learning yoga.

The instructors who have been the most significant models for me have been the instructors who not only live in *their* own bodies, but who have empowered me to live in *mine*. Learning yoga is much more than simply learning a physical skill. I have appreciated certain teachers who, throughout the years, have played a significant role in helping me become more aware of and more sensitive to my body. These individuals may have been excellent technicians, but the greater attraction for me was their grace, their poise, their equanimity, and their ability to inculcate what they knew.

On the other hand, I have encountered instructors whose attitude left something to be desired. Years ago I attended a yoga class taught by a young Indian man who was a disciple of Mr. Iyengar. This man was determined to force his students into the most difficult and uncomfortable poses he could possibly imagine. This is the kind of class in which injuries are likely to happen. At one point the instructor was standing on my back while I was lifting my shoulders and legs in a backward bend. I asked him to please take his foot off my back, because what he was doing did not feel right and he was hurting me. He said, "No. You need this." I said, "Please. It's my body." He said, "No, in my class your body is my body." After he finally removed his foot, I got up and left the class. This unfortunate story dramatizes one teacher's attitude of superiority toward the student. In this class the teacher utterly ignored my experience in my body, which is the most important thing in yoga. What he was presenting was not yoga.

Often when I am presenting asanas to a class, a student will ask me where he "should" feel the stretch. I always respond by asking him where he *does* feel the stretch. I can certainly discuss what the pose is designed to address in terms of developing strength, flexibility, or balance. But any pose is capable of producing a sensation completely different from its basic or ostensible intent. Furthermore, two students might have a totally dissimilar experience in the same yoga stretch, depending on how their bodies are put together, including where the areas of resistance are. As a matter of fact, I'd like to redefine the poses as being more than a stretch to any certain body parts. The larger and more important question that remains is, under this *particular* demand, where does your body seem most reluctant to yield? What information do you get? Where is the movement? Where does energy flow and where does it not flow? What part of your body is learning to let go?

A forward bend, for example, presumably lengthens the back side of the body. Wherever your body resists, however, is where the sensation will be most intense. Finding this place is one of the primary purposes of yoga. It makes sense to me that a student will become particularly aware of the tension in his jaw while doing a forward bend. Because energy moves through our bodies in all of the asanas, when energy gets hung up, when it doesn't move, we can feel it. I see my role as encouraging my students to make these discoveries on their own, rather than as telling them what they should feel. After all, a heightened awareness of your body is one of the most important lessons you should learn from your yoga experience. This is what you glean from your practice, the part that will affect your experience in your body for the rest of your day.

THE TECHNOLOGY OF YOGA

The instructions in this book are designed to accommodate most body types. Certain contraindications, however, may appear in your body. For example, intense pain (especially shooting or nerve pain), dizziness, or the sensation of numbness in your extremities are all messages that the way you are doing a particular stretch is not good for you. If you experience any of these sensations while in a particular pose, come out of the pose. Chances are, the pose itself is not the problem, but the way you are doing the pose is the problem. Guidance from an instructor may enable you to repeat the pose successfully at a later time. Do not run the risk of perpetuating faulty habits, which is the one potential danger of working on your own. Err on the conservative side, especially at the beginning. Moving slowly, paying careful attention to your body's limits, and recognizing signs of pain or discomfort will help you to avoid unnecessary injuries. One of my teachers used to say that if you get hurt doing yoga, then you aren't doing yoga. Gradually, as your body learns to relax, you will find the poses more pleasurable and less intense.

Unlike traditional athletics, in which your performance is measured by speed, duration, length, and so on, yoga is not a contest. If you have been involved with sports, consider reevaluating your approach to them. The values that work on the playing field, are often inappropriate when applied to learning hatha yoga. If you regard yoga as a competition, for example, you are bound to lose. That is, if you force your body into postures for which it is not ready, it will recoil into deeper holding and more resistance. Also, aggression in the poses will greatly increase your chances of injuring your body.

After a long, strenuous race or some other athletic exertion, you might say that you are "out of breath." In yoga, however, we are never out of breath. We always *find* each breath. Even while we are exerting ourselves, while our bodies are being challenged, a steady breath ensures that we are maintaining equanimity. When you are out of breath you often feel upset, exhausted, out of control, or somehow disoriented. The opposite—focusing and centering yourself on each breath—brings about a different reaction, namely relaxation, restfulness, calmness, and a feeling of being in control. In addition, a steady breath brings to the peripheral and deep muscle tissue an uninterrupted stream of oxygen and nutrients necessary to flush out the chemical by-products of chronic tension. This feature is important for relaxation in yoga. In this case, relaxation is an observable physiological event. It is different from and more than the relaxation that people associate with watching television or reading a good book. This relaxation is the object of your attention rather than the by-product of a separate activity.

One more feature of the breath reflects the spiritual and metaphysical aspect of yoga. When you follow each breath, your mind is guided to the present moment. After all, each breath occurs only in present time. Paying attention to that breath lessens or eliminates your mind's attachment to the past and the future. One of my yoga students recently learned that she was much more able to be aware of and release the tension in her body if she moved slowly. She had been unable to focus on her breathing during her former style of moving, which was hyperkinetic and always hurried. Learning to be in present time, especially while focusing on your breath, can be the beginning of a profoundly improved relationship with your body. You may find, like my student did, that this is the best way to learn to release your own tension. Slow movement, and the body awareness that such movement allows, can offset some of the deleterious side effects (physical and otherwise) of "hurry sickness."

Prior to practicing these yoga asanas, bear in mind the following essential points:

1. *Stretching chronic tension in your body is intense.* This is not necessarily a situation to be avoided. Although the intensity is not particularly pleasant, you will gain the most from stretching your body if you are courageous enough to work with the areas that resist. The "negative feedback" you get from your body is not bad news. On the contrary, you are *looking for* the areas in your body where the tissue is stiff, dense, or unyielding. If you find them, you have accomplished one of the primary objectives of doing yoga, namely, to learn how you store tension in your body. If you discover these little patches of resistance, stay with them for at least a few long breaths. Eventually the discomfort will probably melt as a wave of release moves into your body. Tolerating the initial intensity is worth it. If the tension doesn't melt (which it often does, especially given time), you will have a much keener sense of how and where you hold tension. That in itself is extremely valuable. It also helps you put what you have done in a positive framework, which helps you feel successful.

Many novice students move with relative ease through the beginning period, in which the poses feel very intense, into the next phase, which is much more pleasurable. Others require weeks before the body actually enjoys the feeling of stretching. This transition occurs at different times for different people, depending on such factors as age, physical history, tissue quality, and frequency and regularity of practice time. Eventually your body will yield to the demands of the stretches. Regardless of the time required, it is extremely valuable to continue practicing, while your body comes to realize the effect of the yoga.

2. *Learning to relax is an acquirable skill.* You become more proficient with time and practice. If you have stiffness in your back, you can learn to stretch and release it on your own. Gradually, you develop proficiency and mastery in your own body. With practice and time, you can learn to move and stretch in just the right way to relieve yourself of the discomfort associated with habitual ways of holding and tensing your body. You will notice that your stretching becomes more efficient in bringing deep relaxation to your body. Knowing just how to get to your tension will enable you to do the poses that bring about a specific desired result, such as providing relief from a certain kind of pain or stiffness.

Many students feel afraid at first to explore the parts of their bodies where the tension is most intense. This reluctance is related to the fact that pain and stiffness already exist in these parts. Also, these people may not have explored the areas of tension and may fear moving into body parts that they are used to holding. As you gain the necessary courage to stretch, breathe into, and release the tension in your body, you also learn to move your body so as to release these chronic problems and perhaps prevent a recurrence. Trepidations about stretching a stiff neck, for example, may simply be the flip side of the attitude that has caused you to guard and stiffen your neck in the first place.

This is not to suggest a flagrant disregard for the various messages and cues that your body gives you about pain and dysfunction. Effectively

151

deciphering the messages your body constantly gives you comes after much quiet time, when you may be physically active but mentally quiet, for the express purpose of tuning in to your body. Although you may never decode your body flawlessly, you can acquire considerable skill and sensitivity in this arena. In terms of responding to muscle tension, this work gives you options other than habitually pulling even tighter when your body feels stiff. Through yoga you can learn to expand, rather than contract, in response to tension. Thus yoga is a tool for managing and offsetting stress, tension, structural problems, and even some medical problems.

3. *Yoga should always relieve stress, never induce it.* How you regard the time you spend doing yoga will affect its outcome. Any attempt to rush through yoga will only detract from the benefit. If you decide to push yourself too hard, you might become injured rather than relaxed. Moving slowly ensures that you pay attention to your body's potential as well as to its limitations. Yesterday you may have been able to put your hands on the floor in a forward bend, but that may have been before a stressful day at the office or a nine-hour drive to Los Angeles. Today your fingers can just get down to your knees. You can spend time expanding your limits, but the key is to recognize them and work gently in the direction in which you intend to move. In any case, the more attentive you are to your body's needs and limits, the more sophisticated your yoga poses will become. Pay attention. Your body constantly gives you feedback. Work with yourself. Learn to surrender rather than to push. Learn to give in rather than to force. Avoid creating a situation in which you and your body are adversaries. Allow your body to open as a function of your relaxation, rather than of your ambition.

4. *The success you achieve in yoga is not measured by your performance, but by how well you listen and respond to your body's abilities and limitations.* If you touch your toes by pulling your back down, that is, tightening it, you will have missed the opportunity to lengthen and release as you go forward. It's not worth the cost of tightening your body just to be able to touch the floor. By tuning in to the way energy flows through your body, by

becoming aware of the nuances in the ways in which you hold and the ways in which you let go, each asana becomes a vehicle for learning more about how you live in the body that is yours. Therein lies the success of each yoga stretch.

5. *Time is critical in your ability to produce desirable changes in your body.* How much time you spend learning the yoga stretches can be a fairly simple decision. What are your goals? How much impact do the tension and stiffness in your body have on your daily experience of living? How *important* is it to you to make these changes? As in learning any new art form, the results you achieve are directly proportional to the number of hours you put into your discipline. If the going is slow, breathe away your frustration to the best of your ability. If you have never practiced stretching your body before, why expect to be an expert on the first day? And if your personal history includes aggressive athletics, injuries, illness, or abuse, realize that you have chosen to open your body and that it will be particularly challenging for you. More power to you.

6. *Working with gravity will greatly facilitate your ability to develop flexibility and learn to relax.* Yoga teaches us to allow energy to move through our bodies along the path of least resistance. This is a model for connecting physically and energetically through our physical bodies to our environment and to our Earth. It is obvious that certain stretches require strength, some focus primarily on flexibility, and others are a blend of both. The ones that require relatively little or no actual strength I call "gravity poses." In these poses, gravity does all the work. Your only job is to figure out how to let go.

In *Awakening the Spine*, Vanda Scaravelli writes,

> What is that binding force that holds the many worlds together and with its intensity also attracts us to each other? Can we call it Gravity, Energy, Love?[1]

Gravity provides the ultimate support for our bodies to learn to let go of holding. While doing yoga, if we allow the floor to support us, if we let gravity hold us, then holding ourselves becomes superfluous.

If you are angry or upset while you are doing yoga, use the time to calm your emotional body. Lie on your back and breathe deeply for about five minutes, rather than beginning your yoga asanas in an agitated state of mind. Relaxation through breathing will allow you to approach the asanas from a calmer perspective and thus avoid injuring yourself. Stretching and breathing can be a miraculous help to you in "blowing off steam." I have worked through my share of feeling angry and upset while doing yoga, so I know that this can be effective and powerful. But you must avoid introjecting the anger back into your body, thereby internalizing the stress even deeper into your musculature and back into yourself. If yoga is stressful, then it is not yoga.

If you happen to be injured or debilitated from an illness or a sports- or job-related accident, your yoga poses will look and feel quite different for a while. The limitations that your body presents to you are real, and you must be willing to listen closely to what your body is telling you. Dealing with any acute problem requires that you slow down even more. Your body at this time has unique needs that you can meet through concentration and focus. If you move too quickly, you will miss the subtle but important cues from your body. Dealing effectively with pain or dysfunction requires that you be even more aware than you are at a time when your body is more open, more resilient, and less vulnerable.

Don't try to "get rid" of the injury. Rather, see yourself reowning and reintegrating the body part in question. Your body will react more favorably to this approach. In yoga, a hurt knee is viewed as the area in the middle of your leg, with two major joints at either end (hip and ankle). The way in which you organize your entire leg from the inside is key to handling and releasing any problems in the knee. Think of the injury of the knee as an event of the leg, and not simply of the knee. You will receive information from elsewhere in your body that is pertinent to the primary injury. A tightness in your hamstrings, for example, may be traced to the pain behind your knee.

And because your hamstrings are attached to the ischial tuberosities (sitting bones), the tightness in your hamstrings may be noticeably connected to a tightness in your hip.

Yoga is an excellent way to work on compensations, that is, problems in your body that result from favoring or in some way disorganizing around a weakness, pain, or stiffness elsewhere in your body. A sprained ankle may lead to a stiff hip on the opposite side of the body six weeks after the original sprain. Avoiding the use of the ankle puts undue strain on the side opposite to the sprain itself. Structural work in both yoga and Rolfing frequently focuses on these compensations.

In all poses, you can feel where your body has shortened or rotated in areas where there are compensations in the soft tissue. It is valuable to pay close attention to these areas of holding and limitation. As a rule of thumb, in an area where it was your intention to lengthen your body, and your body shortened, this is where the work is for you in this particular pose. Getting an even stretch from side to side and from front to back ensures that the release moves through your body. Working in a mindful way provides a true reading of the asymmetries and imbalances to be treated.

Dr. Rolf used to say, "The body is a plastic medium." Your body can and will change. The stretches will become more agreeable and less uncomfortable, and your body will gradually learn to contain more energy and more pleasure. The more you provide yourself with the right conditions, the more your body will provide you with a comfortable and supportive place to live, move, and breathe. Remember to regard the discovery of *how* you hold, the particulars of your tension patterns, as progress. They too are part of self-discovery.

* * * * *

Doing yoga is similar to the "end feel" approach in Rolfing. The following examples illustrate how this works. As a Rolfer, I sit at the client's foot or hip to feel the connection to the knee by using my hands, eyes, and intuition. Or I sit at the client's head, feeling the range of motion in the cervical vertebrae and observing how the tightness in the neck is connected to tightness in the sacrum and something going on in the arms. I call this a "line of tension." The opposite is also true, in which case the release in the sacrum is related to the release in the cervical region, and so on. This is called a "line of energy." In the case of the knee, there is evidence of the injury in the two distal joints and can be treated from either end. The injury is transmitted beyond the hurt joint. I touch or manipulate the ankle while feeling for any disruption between the ankle and the knee, including in the knee. A practiced yogi treats his body with the same broad perspective and a similar sensitivity to the structural considerations.

If you get injured, you may find it valuable to lie on the floor and make micromovements with your neck and your spine, or wherever the injury is. Your body is exploring a range of motion in a completely nonresistant field. This has enormous healing capacity in terms of self-correcting problems in your body. Even though there has been damage in terms of strains or contractures, with the micromovements your consciousness lives in the place where energy still flows. When you focus your mind in this way, your body is naturally prone to explore release rather than to limit itself further. While you are in the yoga stretches, these micromovements enable you to go deeper into surrender.

Practice breathing and visualizing your body mending, exploring the areas of release with your mind. That may be your yoga during a time when your body is going through its healing. Be careful not to impose any stress whatsoever on your body. Working intensively, with great effort and vigor, is counterproductive when you are self-treating an acute injury. If you are the type who tends to overwork your body, this may be the ultimate test in letting go: Refraining from working your body so hard so as to compound the stresses upon it, and being willing to change how you move are the new lessons.

WORKING WITH YOUR ROLFER

You and your Rolfer work as a team toward the attainment of specific, identifiable objectives with regard to your body. These goals include the proper distribution of your weight within the gravitational field, a sense of length and overall body alignment, and a reorganization of the connective tissue to free your body of superficial and deep restrictions. The Rolfer's knowledge, the fact that you are being touched deeply, and the information you receive from an objective professional add up to some rather significant influences on your body. If you select a Rolfer who is oriented toward teaching you about your body, you are especially likely to gain important and useful information.

One of the objectives of this book is to provide a sequence of yoga postures that combine with Rolfing to produce a synergistic entity more potent than either of the therapies alone would produce. By following this series, you become more involved in and take more responsibility for producing the changes toward which you and your Rolfer are working so diligently. And working with a competent and professional yoga instructor and a certified Rolfer will enhance the self-discoveries and improvements on your body that you find through yoga. The assistance of a competent professional (or professionals) is invaluable.

If you are currently being Rolfed, I encourage you to share the discoveries you make about your body through yoga with your Rolfer. The feedback you get about your body from stretching is as valuable for the Rolfer as it is for you. For example, you may never have noticed that your left hip rotates more easily than your right hip does. Or perhaps you have just learned that your right arm is much more supple at the shoulder joint than your left arm and shoulder are when your arms are raised overhead. Maybe it is harder to let go on your left side. Your Rolfer can use this information to further personalize your body therapy. Because the two systems are so naturally compatible, your insights will help your Rolfer understand your body in ways that will ultimately enhance her ability to give your body what it needs. I have had some excellent sessions during which a Rolfer actually worked on my body while I stretched. The Rolfer was able to use her hands to help me work through and release some restrictions in my body. The work was extremely helpful, particularly when these restrictions were problems that had become chronic. Working in this fashion feels incredibly good. The results have always been significant in terms of my capacity to let go on a deeper level, because I was being touched and supported in areas where I knew I would have difficulty releasing tension when working alone.

ONE FINAL CONSIDERATION

Everybody—every *body*—is different. Therefore it would not be possible to produce a series of yoga asanas that are appropriate and effective for all individuals. It simply can't be done. As an illustration, imagine ten different sufferers of back pain. More than ten different configurations of problems in the muscles, bones, ligaments, and connective tissue contribute to back problems. Each different back would indicate different stretches or strengthening exercises to help bring relief from the problems. The same dilemma exists in applying yoga for different types of postural problems.

Rounded shoulders can be the result of one or more of a group of potentially unrelated causes in the structure and connective tissue.

For this reason, I encourage you to watch your body carefully while stretching it according to the directions in these pages. I have selected asanas that are appropriate for most body types. Even if the yoga stretch is intense and not particularly pleasurable, you can learn to distinguish whether the pose is beneficial or harmful to your body. If there is any sense of release or relief, if you can feel your body open to a new level of strength or flexibility, the overwhelming odds are that you are on to something that will ultimately have a positive effect on your body. A yank, a sharp pain, an intensely uncomfortable feeling that is more than you can work with or breathe with is contraindicated. Learning to back off at times is necessary. Your body might have different requirements than those postures outlined in the chapter that follows can provide. Keep yourself tuned in to the effects as you experience them in your body. Be sure you have read chapter 13 carefully. Despite the general nature of a series of yoga stretches of this kind, this approach to lengthening and balancing your body can be tremendously valuable. Highly personalized work, however, can come only from a trained professional who is able to work with your body in a hands-on, individualized manner.

Concentration helps you get the most out of each moment that you work on your body. Ideally, every minute you are practicing yoga stretches, you are learning about yourself: how you resist, how you let go, how your body tells your life story, and how you have learned to express yourself. As you learn to read your own body, you gain access to information that will shed light on virtually every experience you may have.

159

13

Chapter **THIRTEEN**

Yoga Asanas to Accompany the Basic Rolfing Series

The following yoga asanas, or postures, are designed to complement the basic Rolfing series. The goals of the Rolfing sequence are similar to the objectives of the following combination of yoga postures, especially from a structural point of view. To my knowledge, I am the first person to present yoga with an overall view toward balancing the whole body. Typically in yoga books, the postures are grouped into standing poses, forward bends, twists, arm balances, inverted poses, and backward bending poses. Or they are categorized according to types of situations they address: "Yoga for Premenstrual Syndrome," "Yoga for Back Pain," "Yoga for Runners," and the like. The poses in the following pages, however, are put together expressly for the purpose of balancing and realigning your entire body.

Instructions for how to use this information have appeared throughout the previous chapters, particularly in chapter 12. This chapter is divided into sessions, and the objective of each corresponds to the objectives of the Rolfing hour with the same number. Share this information with your Rolfer if you are going through that process.

If you do not have a Rolfer but would like to find one, contact The Rolf Institute for names of Rolfers in your geographical area. You can write to the Rolf Institute at P.O. Box 1868, Boulder, Colorado, 94306. The phone number is 1-800-530-8875. If you are already being Rolfed and are looking for a yoga teacher, the *Yoga Journal*, published in Berkeley, California, is an excellent resource. It publishes a directory of yoga teachers that is extremely helpful. The number in Berkeley is 510-841-9200.

SESSION ONE

The first Rolfing hour introduces methods of lessening the pressure in the entire musculoskeletal system. My goals in this hour include initially balancing the shoulder girdle and hip girdle. As a result, the client becomes more aware of the appropriate fit between the muscular and the bony compartments of the shoulders and the hips. I loosen the diaphragm to enable the body to breathe fully throughout subsequent sessions. Lengthening the spine gives the client the sense of more room in the back side of the body. This process is sometimes referred to as "removing the first layer of the wetsuit."

CHILD'S POSE

This stretch is gentle or intense, depending on the relative flexibility of your hips, lower back, and entire spine. Sit comfortably on your heels. If you experience too much pain, discomfort, or tightness in your legs, knees, or feet, try putting a pillow under your hips (see figure 13-1a) or under your feet (see figure 13-1b). The pillow is intended to provide support and comfort. It gives you something to sit on if your hips don't rest easily on your heels or if the tops of your feet don't reach the floor. Air offers no support. If you have no physical surface on which to rest your body, you are more apt to hold yourself up. This then becomes the part of your body that doesn't lengthen. This is where you need to give your body extra support: literally, something to sit on. Experiment with the pillows so that you can find ways to increase your comfort, thus enabling yourself to achieve more flexibility.

As you reach out with your torso, lengthen the front as well as the back of your body. Be sure to allow the area under your ribs to expand. Avoid rounding your back and shortening between the base of your ribs and your hips. Lengthen here. As you place your torso on your legs, reach out as far as your spine can stretch. Release the area between your shoulder blades, so that your arms fall comfortably by your side. Turn your palms up toward the ceiling. (See figure 13-1c.)

Figure 13-1a: Sit on your heels. Put a pillow under your hips for greater comfort.

Figure 13-1b: Sit on your heels. Put a pillow under your feet.

Figure 13-1c: Place your torso on your legs, reach out as far as your spine can stretch. Turn your palms up toward the ceiling.

Variation 1. If you know that your spine is inclined posterior at the level of the lumbar vertebrae (the opposite of a swayback), try this variation. Widen your knees and move your buttocks toward the ceiling. Allow your lower abdominal area to drop gently toward the floor as you reach upward with your hips. The shape of your lower back will drop down, the opposite of what happens in the previous stretch. As in the first pose, lengthen your spine by reaching out with your arms and your entire back. Once your spine has lengthened, allow your buttocks to drop down to your heels. (See figure 13-1d.)

Figure 13-1d: Widen your knees. Stretch your spine forward as you drop your belly down to the floor.

Variation 2: When you begin this stretch, place your body one arm's length from a couch, a bed, or some heavy object of approximately equal height. Reach overhead with your arms in order to place your hands shoulder width apart. Placing your hands firmly, reach back with your entire spine, moving from the hips. As your arms move over your head, you will experience a wonderful stretch at the tops of your shoulders. There should be distance from your shoulders to your ears: Do not scrunch here. In this pose, your spine lengthens. This is a dynamic stretch in that your body moves deliberately in two directions, both in opposition from the center. (See figure 13-1e.)

Figure 13-1e: Place your body approximately one arm's length from a couch, a bed, or some heavy object of approximately equal height. Place your hands shoulder width apart, arms reaching overhead. Moving from the hips, stretch your spine away from your arms.

SESSION TWO

The second Rolfing hour has several objectives. The first pertains to the alignment of the feet and legs. In addition to working on the lower half of the body, it is my goal in the second hour to help the client achieve a lengthening along the front of the spine. As the feet open across the major hinges (ankles, heels, and metatarsals), the direction of the leg bones changes with relation to the horizontal surface (the floor) upon which the feet are placed. In other words, the realignment of the feet and legs begins to allow the legs to become more vertical. Thus the center of gravity is less inclined to be pushed forward or held back, which is another way of saying there is less muscle tension in the legs and pelvis. It is this same centering of the body's weight, together with the vertical alignment of the legs, to the lengthening of the back of the body (first hour), and the lengthening of the front of the body (second hour) that begins to shift the body's relationship to the gravitational field. The lengthening and releasing of layers of connective tissue that have previously distorted the body's alignment lead to this shift. I accomplish this in the second hour by softening the area between the lower leg bones (tibia and fibula), opening the joints of the feet, aligning the thighs and hips, and stretching and releasing tension from the prevertebral space (the area in front of the spine). As early as the second Rolfing session, then, the *relationships* between the front and back and between the top and bottom of the body are addressed.

LEG-BALANCING POSE

Stand opposite a staircase or a flat surface of some kind, that is approximately two feet high. A set of steps is ideal because of the graduated ascending elevation, or you can use varied pieces of heavy furniture, each at a different level. Experiment with your level of flexibility to determine which height is right for you. Your size and leg length are also factors. Stand approximately one leg length away from the surface, with all ten toes and both hips facing the steps (or furniture). Without disturbing or rotating the bottom leg and hip, lift the first leg at the knee. Stretch it from the hip, extending through the heel. Your knee remains straight, and you stretch your heel out. Lengthening the tendons and ligaments behind your calcaneus (heel bone) enables you to use your heels for more stability and a more efficient posture. (See figure 13-2a.) The higher surface requires more flexibility to your hips.

Figure 13-2a: Elevate one leg while dropping the hip down on that same side. The standing leg and foot remain facing forward.

As you stretch through the lifted leg, be aware of your overall alignment, especially through your spine. The idea in this pose is that your hip flexes (on the side of the leg that is lifted) without disturbing the rest of your body. In other words, as your hip and hamstrings lengthen, the rest of your body remains at rest. (The ability to do this will come in handy as you stand, walk, or sit.) The hip on the side of the lifted leg continues to drop down.

As you release and lengthen your leg, begin to focus on allowing more length to move into your spine. One way to achieve this is by lifting your arms overhead. As you do this, be careful to drop and soften your shoulders. The rotation of the shoulders and abduction of the arms (moving the arms away from the midline) can occur without elevation of the scapulae. With your arms overhead you can easily bring length to the front of your spine; the front lengthens without your back shortening. This lengthening is the result of your releasing the holding in the front, not of your tightening the back. Breathe deeply into your spine, simultaneous with dropping through the hip of the lifted leg and the tops of both shoulders.

Moving your eyes only (that is, without disturbing the restful position of your head on the top of your body), look down at the leg you have lifted. Notice any deviations in terms of the alignment of the leg. If you perceive any torques or twists, can you use the musculature of your leg to lengthen what is short and derotate what is rotated? Be careful to not favor the standing leg. Continue to drop through the hip of the lifted leg.

The more contact between your standing foot and the floor, the better the alignment of the bottom leg. This further ensures that the musculature of the leg is loose. As you increase the range of motion in your pelvis and the flexibility in your legs and hips, gradually place your lifted leg and foot on higher surfaces. Do not be overly ambitious. It is more important to achieve structural balance than to raise the lifted leg higher.

To discover the functional benefit of this stretch, walk a bit after completing the first side. Observe the two sides of your body. What influence has this particular stretch had on your body? Has some shift occurred that you can observe while walking? Make these observations throughout the time you practice this series of yoga stretches. The more aware you are of the effect of the asana, the more likely you will be to incorporate these positive changes into your life throughout the rest of the day, and between yoga sessions.

Repeat the entire series with the other side.

Variation: Lie down on your back, with both legs relaxed on the floor. Bending at one hip, lift the first leg straight toward the ceiling. Take hold of the outer edge of the foot of the elevated leg. (See figure 13-2b.) If you are unable to reach your foot without rounding your shoulders, put a belt around the bottom of your foot. (See figure 13-2c.) Remember that everything lengthens. Hold on to two ends of the belt with both hands while keeping your back at rest on the floor. Keep your hands separate; this helps open the chest and relax the shoulders. The bottom leg continues to lengthen on the floor. The lifted leg stretches toward the ceiling without disturbing the spine. The hip on the lifted-leg side flexes; the hip on the lower-leg side extends; the spine remains neutral.

Figure 13-2b: Lie on your back. Flex one hip, bringing the straight leg toward your face. The other leg remains at rest on the floor. Relax your shoulders.

Learning the differences among the various anatomical positions of your body enables you to make corrections and adjustments more effectively. You have a tangible frame of reference for the alignment of your body. The cue to "flex your hip" requires a different response than the cue to "flex your spine." (See figures 13-2d and 13-2e respectively.) An understanding of how your body works is a tool that can help you make structural corrections on your own.

Figure 13-2c: If you have difficulty reaching your foot without rounding your shoulders, use a belt around the foot of the lifted leg. Bring your hand as close as you can to your foot while the shoulder remains at rest on the floor.

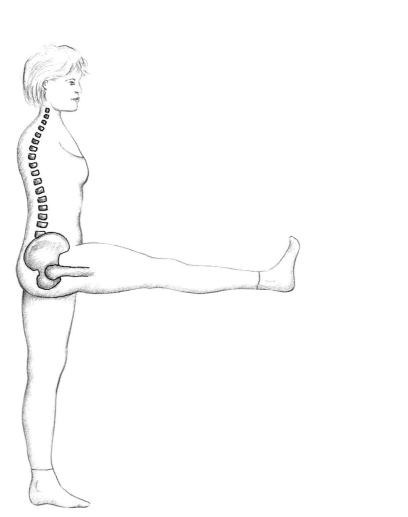

Figure 13-2d: Hip flexion

As the lifted leg presses toward the ceiling, continue to rest your body on the floor. Even as you reach your arms toward the foot of the lifted leg, the back side of your body surrenders to gravity. Avoid rounding your back or flexing the front of your body as you move your hands toward your foot. In fact, reach your arms only as far as you can without compromising your ability to relax your entire upper body on the floor. You can use the belt around the foot of the lifted leg to secure the elevated position of this leg. Even though your hip flexes, the hip flexors remain soft. Understanding this concept enables you to move according to the Rolf principles of movement. With this approach, your body lengthens while it moves. This contradicts the traditional view of kinesiology that your body contracts in order to make even the simplest of moves. In this stretch, just as in the previous asana, you lengthen your entire body, not just the part being stretched.

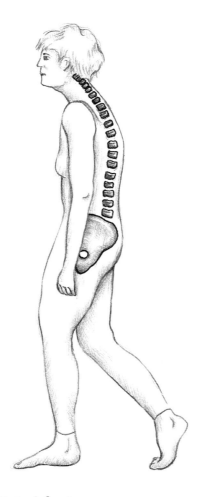

Figure 13-2e: Spinal flexion

SESSION THREE

In the third Rolfing hour, I look at the sides of the torso, shoulders, and hips. I examine the ribs for their position with relation to the spine and the overall balance of the torso. Often I deal with chronic back problems in this hour. Reorganizing the ribs and spine releases pain and stiffness in the back. I also look at the depth of the body from front to back. If the client is compressing his body from front to back, I will deal with that. When the sides are opened, the body gains more depth. Often a client reports having more room in the torso for breathing and moving as a result of the work in the third hour.

Many of the restrictions in your body come from habits in your movement patterns. For example, perhaps you always hike your shoulders towards your ears when pulling on a pair of trousers, a move that is inefficient and tends to stiffen the trapezius muscle. The beauty of yoga is that it exposes those restrictions. Thus you learn where the potential for change is the greatest. If you keep to a strictly sedentary routine, you may never discover the narrowness of the range in which you move. In the third Rolfing hour, opening up the sides of your body allows your spine to flex laterally. (See figure 13-3a.) And although this is not a particularly difficult or complicated move, having this as an option has a positive effect on all of your movement. When your body releases its restrictions anywhere, even the most basic activities, such as brushing your teeth or tying your shoes, become easier and more graceful.

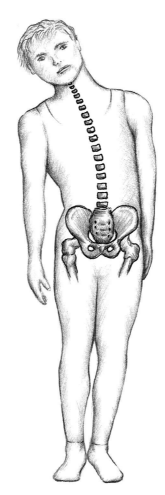

Figure 13-3a: Lateral flexion of the spine.

SIDE GATE POSE

Begin by kneeling on both knees. Keeping both hips facing forward, stretch one leg out to the side, in line with both hips. Place your heel on the floor as you open the pelvis at the base. To accomplish this, shift your pelvis from side to side: Do not bend forward from here. Place your arm down by the side of the bent leg. Turn your other hand upward as it rests on the leg stretched to the side. After a full inhalation, stretch from your hips as you move your torso out over the stretched leg. Do not bend your spine forward. This is a lateral bend, not a forward flexion. (See figure 13-3b.) Concentrate on releasing and lengthening from the hip through the ribs and shoulder of the bent-knee side. Stretch your arm overhead as you reach toward your foot on the stretched-leg side. Your body remains in line with your hips and straight leg. Open your waistline. Allow your ribs to open at their base. Your lower back continues to lengthen. Your pelvis is neither tucked under nor tipped forward. Get a sense, from the inside, of your body being in alignment. When your body is in balance, you can feel it. More energy flows, and pressure and internal resistance decrease. An increased flow of energy is definitely something you can feel.

The arm of the bent-leg side reaches overhead, avoiding compression through the trapezius by keeping the shoulder down. To intensify the stretch, deliberately lengthen at the waistline and at the crest of the ilium (hip bone). As you release into the intensity, be sure you are lengthening your entire body. Be aware of the hip of the straight-leg side. By allowing your hip to open, you free your spine to stretch farther to the side.

179

Figure 13-3b: Side Gate Pose. This is a lateral bend, not a forward flexion.

Variation: Stand one arm's length from the wall. With the side of your body to the wall, elevate your arm and place your hand at shoulder height on the wall, fingers pointing toward the ceiling. Push your body away from the wall, moving from your hips. The arm on the side away from the wall lifts overhead, and then toward the wall. Imagine an opening from the outer ankle, through the lateral portion of the knee, and through the hip, torso, and shoulder. The entire side of your body lengthens as it moves away from the wall. Push the wall away with your hand. For added openness, press down the heel of the foot that is farther from the wall. Create as much length in your body as possible. (See figure 13-3c.) Feel your waistline open on the side that faces away from the wall. Drop your head toward the wall side of your body to increase the stretch. Both shoulders should relax downward.

Figure 13-3c: The entire side of your body lengthens as it moves away from the wall.

SESSION FOUR

The fourth Rolfing hour begins a deeper organization around the pelvis, the adductors of the inner thighs, and the medial portion of the lower legs. Typically in the fourth hour, I look at my client's body to determine where the structure has holding patterns, from the pelvic floor to the feet. Holding patterns are found in the pelvis in various forms. Many theories have evolved to explain these variations in structural misalignment. Some include psychological explanations for holding tension in the legs, perineum, and buttocks. Bowed legs, for example, would strongly indicate that the person needed fourth-hour work. And on a psychological level, this particular structural fixation might reflect the individual's need to separate from the mother, to, in fact, distance himself from his mother. The client and I may therefore work together on more than one level simultaneously.

Interpreting a person's holding patterns psychologically is not a fixed science. In this example, bowed legs may be related to the client's personal history, or the condition may be purely structural. In all cases, the interpretation is offered to the client as a way for him to explore that part of himself. If holding the shoulders up is associated with held-in fear, then the client can consider whether any emotions, fear or otherwise, are released when his shoulders drop down. This information is not used for diagnosis, but rather as a tool for gaining insight into the body.

Deep reorganization of the legs and pelvic floor inevitably affects the torso. A pronounced imbalance in the way each leg articulates with the hip bones, for example, rarely begins and ends in the hips. In terms of the overall structure, a pair of unmatched hip joints is significant. The misshapenness and relative misalignment of the torso is invariably related to an imbalance in the underlying structure. Therefore, fourth-hour work not only takes into

183

consideration alignment issues presented by the hips, legs, and feet, but establishes congruence and support between the lower and upper halves of the body. As we shall soon see, these objectives are explored from an even more complex perspective in the fifth hour.

BUTTERFLY POSE

Sit comfortably on the floor, with your weight on the sitting bones (ischial tuberosities). Imagine a triangle forming. The three points of the triangle are the two sitting bones in the back and the point from which a plumb line drops down from your pubic bone. Placing your weight in the center of that triangle ensures that your weight is well balanced. (See figure 13-4a.) When you sit on this triangle, your body is more able to lengthen in the front and back simultaneously.

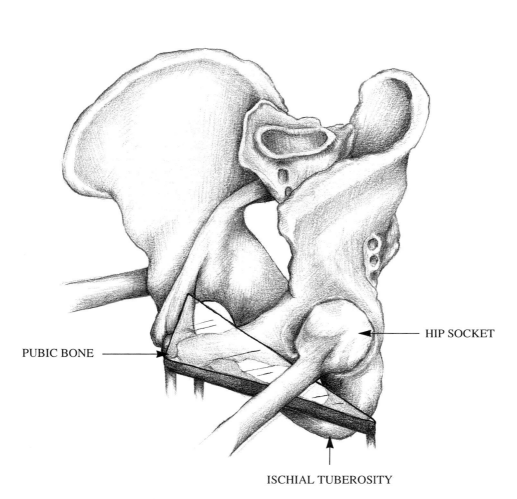

PUBIC BONE

HIP SOCKET

ISCHIAL TUBEROSITY

Figure 13-4a: The sitting triangle.

On the other hand, sitting inefficiently can shorten your body and distribute the weight unevenly, causing imbalance and tightness. One such way of sitting is with your weight rolled back on the fleshy part of your buttocks. Sitting comfortably in this position is nothing short of impossible. The shortness in the front of your body counterbalances any attempt to sit tall or erect by pulling your body down and allowing your center of gravity to fall toward the back of your spine. (See figure 13-4b.) Pitching your weight forward, with your hips rolled forward of the sitting bones and the pubic bone pulled down toward the floor, presents a different problem. Your body may look open and extended, but that is only on the front side. The shortness on the back side produces fatigue and discomfort, especially if you sit this way for extended periods of time. (See figure 13-4c.)

In the butterfly pose, you set your body up to maximize the natural and internal length from deep in the pelvic floor. Having established yourself on your triangle, bend your legs and bring the soles of your feet together, heels close to the perineum. Drop your knees down to the floor. Allow your hips to open. (See figure 13-4d.) Notice the connection between your ability to release in the adductor region (inner thighs) and the flow of energy and release of tension in your belly, chest, shoulders, back, and neck. In other words, your hips are flexible to the extent that you can relax the rest of your body. As you release tension in your belly, chest, shoulders, back, and neck, your legs will continue their release in the direction toward the floor. If you feel any strain in your lower back, shift your weight forward and back, making tiny adjustments in order to find what is most comfortable. If your body is uncomfortable, rest on the front edge of a folded blanket. Sitting right on your bottom is easier with your hips elevated slightly with relation to your legs. This makes it easier to drop your knees out. Another helpful aid are pillows placed under your knees as well as under your perineum. (Air can not support you!) Resting your legs on the surface of the pillow makes it considerably easier for you to relax your legs and open your pelvis. (See figure 13-4e.)

Figure 13-4b: Shortness in the front of your body counterbalances any attempt to sit tall.

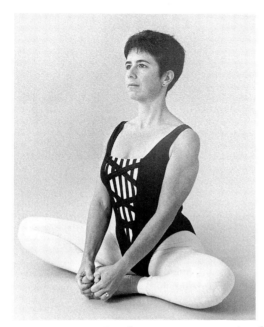

Figure 13-4c: Pitching your weight forward causes shortness on the back, as well as fatigue and discomfort.

Figure 13-4d: In the Butterfly Pose, your knees drop to the floor as you allow your hips to open.

Figure 13-4e: Rest your legs on the surface of the pillow to allow your legs to relax and your pelvis to open.

Variation 1: This alternative is an excellent way to further release the hips while providing support to the back. Lie down on your back, with your hips against the wall. Be sure that your nose, your sternum, and your navel are in a straight, 90-degree line with relations to the wall.

Bend your knees, as in the butterfly pose. This time, drop your heels down toward your perineum as your knees move gently toward the wall. You can use your hands against your knees for extra weight to help open the hips. Continue to lengthen and relax the entire back side of your body. Just as in the seated version of the butterfly pose, the suppleness of your back enables your hips to open more easily. A slow, steady, full breath also helps. As your knees move toward the wall, continue to allow your sacrum to rest on the floor. (See figure 13-4f.)

Figure 13-4f: Butterfly Variation 1. With your back at rest on the floor, it may be easier to open your pelvis.

Variation 2: Remain on your back, with the soles of your feet still touching, your toes lightly against the wall. This time, allow your knees to move down toward the floor. (See figure 13-4g.) If your knees do not touch the floor, place a pillow on the outside of each leg. Since the air does not provide any support, the pillow allows your leg to drop onto some surface. You will probably feel much safer if you let go with this kind of support. (See figure 13-4h.) Again, if you feel any tightness in your back, concentrate on lengthening and relaxing your back toward the floor. Of your back feels arched, lower it down gradually; the floor will support you as your body rests. Do not push your lumbar muscles back. This push, which is the only way to forcibly move the back down, would shorten the front. This tightening of the front of your body would inhibit the lengthening of the adductors and would therefore be counterproductive for this particular stretch.

Figure 13-4g: Butterfly Variation 2. Rest your knees on the floor, bottoms of your feet together. Let your pelvis remain close to the wall. Soften your lower back on the floor.

Figure 13-4h: Same as Butterfly Variation 2. Rest your knees on a pillow.

Repeating the variation from the first hour, with your legs stretched up against the wall, would be ideal at this time. Now, in addition to allowing your legs to lengthen and your sacrum to drop to the floor, become aware of how each hip joint must release from the inside in order for your legs to float toward the ceiling. In other words, do the same stretch, but move your awareness from your legs into your hips and, indeed, into the joints themselves. With your legs resting against the wall, you do not need to harden or shorten the space surrounding the hip joints. Explore the possibility of giving your legs over to the wall rather than holding them there by tightening your hips. Releasing your legs is easiest when the rest of your body has relaxed. Dr. Rolf spoke about this as lengthening while moving. Your hips are in flexion, but your hip flexors are soft and naturally in their resting length.

You need to play with these ideas in order for them to make any sense. At first, these poses may seem to be considerable work—and they are, as long as your body persists in shortening and tightening in old, familiar ways. The less you hold, the less effort you experience in each yoga stretch. In the beginning, the difficulty may keep you from wanting to continue with the asanas, but it is well worth waiting for your body to adjust to the demands of the stretches. As an instructor, there is nothing more rewarding than to see a student rejoice in the positive changes he feels in his body, changes that are the pay-off from having practiced in earnest, in spite of the initial challenges and difficulties.

WIDE-ANGLE STRETCH

In order to begin to let go in the pelvis, bring your hands behind you, next to your thighs. Take your weight through your hands. Widen your legs. Lift your hips off the floor as you drop the front of your pelvis forward. Move gradually, allowing the front to remain open. (See figure 13-4i.) By bringing the pubic bone down, you have allowed the distance from the origin to the insertion of the adductors to lengthen. This is ideal and, ultimately, one of the objectives of this yoga asana. When you place your buttocks back on the floor, the stretch is more intense and your legs are more apt to lengthen. Stretch through your heels. If your legs are still not being stretched, widen at the hips by bringing your feet farther and farther apart. Allow your legs to straighten out as much as possible.

Figure 13-4i: Take your weight through your hands. Widen your legs. Lift your hips off the floor as you drop the front of your pelvis forward.

Sit on your sitting bones. Roll forward slightly as your pubic bone moves down toward the floor. Stretching from the adductors (medial thighs), widen your legs and open your hips. If you have never attempted a stretch like this before, don't be surprised if your hips appear to be in shock from the high demand of the position. In our culture, because we sit primarily in chairs (as opposed to sitting on the ground, or in Indian fashion), you need to go out of your way to get such a deep opening and release in the hip joints and inner thighs. Typically, in your daily routine, you would not have the chance to stretch and open your body in this way. Be sure to lower your body down slowly. (See figure 13-4j.)

Figure 13-4j: Sit on your sitting bones. Roll forward slightly as your pubic bone moves down toward the floor. Move gradually to keep the front open.

It is through the lengthening of your spine and the gradual opening of your pelvis that your torso comes toward the floor. Ironically, you will stretch farther if you are guided by feelings of surrender, rather than by ambition. Because it is your intention to stretch your spine forward, notice if your spine inadvertently moves back. And you can notice this because it feels different to lengthen your spine than it does to compress it. Feeling your back tighten is a reminder to move forward only as your body lengthens, taking up the slack as you feel yourself letting go. It's not worth compensating your body for some external goal, such as bringing your body to the floor. The more you approach these stretches as a *process*, rather than as a *goal*, the more your body will respond favorably in the various positions.

To facilitate an even deeper release in your legs and hips, be sure your weight is slightly forward from the ischial tuberosities. The adductors, which are being stretched in this position, are attached to the ramus of the tuberosities. If your weight is pulled back, you are actually preventing yourself from getting a deep stretch to the adductors. The "tucking under" of the pelvis brings the pubic bone upward. This shortens the adductors and makes it impossible to stretch the inner thighs. You are, in effect, pulling in the opposite direction from the intended stretch. By lengthening the front of the spine, you allow the sitting bones to be under you. This pose is ideal for internalizing a sense of the structural connection between the pelvis and the torso. (See figure 13-4k.)

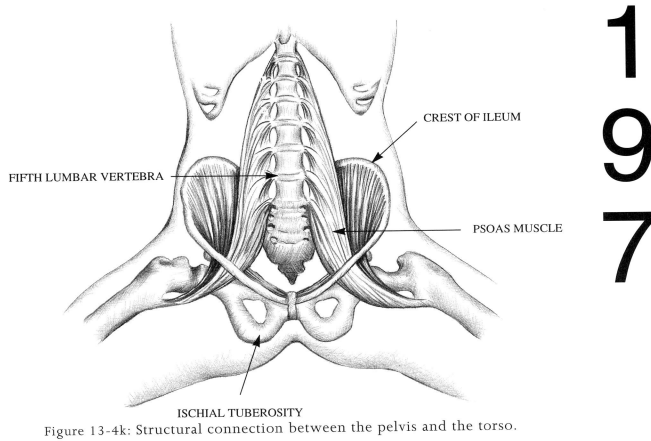

FIFTH LUMBAR VERTEBRA

CREST OF ILEUM

PSOAS MUSCLE

ISCHIAL TUBEROSITY

Figure 13-4k: Structural connection between the pelvis and the torso.

This same stretch can be accomplished by turning your body around 90 degrees, so that your feet and legs are against the wall and your back is against the floor. Get your buttocks as close to the wall as you can. This ensures that you will bend from the hip joints and not from the spine. The beauty of this position is that your spine is fully extended and at rest on the floor. This affects your pelvis in general and your medial thighs in particular by making it easier to relax and open to the stretch. Gravity does a wonderful job of helping your feet to gradually inch toward the floor. (See figure 13-41.) Be sure to breathe to help release the tension.

Figure 13-41: Your feet and legs are against the wall. Your back is against the floor. Get your buttocks close to the wall. Let gravity take your legs down.

As your body becomes more aligned and more flexible, you will notice that resting your legs on the floor without their twisting or pulling becomes easier. This feeling throughout your entire body, during a variety of yoga stretches, is the ultimate goal of this series. Your body's ability to adapt without resistance in a number of different stretches clearly indicates your achievement of some definite and positive structural change. The permanence of this change is completely up to you. The frequency with which you practice and the diligence with which you *handle and release the stresses that inevitably creep into your body* determine the long-lasting benefits of yoga. There is no arrival point in terms of achieving a balanced body. The same is true in Rolfing. Like life, this is work in progress.

The wide-angle stretch, then, can affect you in different ways, depending on the particular structural type of your body. If your legs are rotated externally, your body may be inclined to shorten along the anterior aspect of the lumbar vertebrae. This configuration gives a certain look to your body and presents particular limitations to your flexibility. (See figure 13-4m.) In this case, your legs will roll in slightly as your pelvis becomes horizontal and you open your adductors. You have pulled away from the holding bias in your body. In order to compensate for this demand, your body may shorten elsewhere, at the "other end" of the pattern. This is exactly the kind of data you look for when you stretch. Remember, the pulls and the tugs are not bad, so do not judge them negatively.

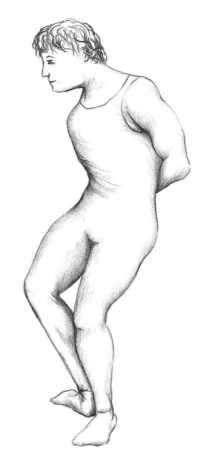

Figure 13-4m: External body type.

If your legs are predisposed to an internal rotation, you may find that your body is prone to shorten along the front of the lumbar spine, which may be inclined to a swayback. In an internal rotation, the pubic ramus is pulled posterior (toward the back of the body.) Again, the shape of and limitations in your body reflect the particulars of this pattern. (See figure 13-4n.) When you sit, the adductors may be taut, thus making it difficult to release the bend out of the legs. Here is an excellent opportunity to employ gravity to help you gradually coax the legs straight. If this describes your body, your legs will roll out slightly as you soften and lengthen the lumbar muscles and spine, and fall back on the sitting bones. In other words, your legs demonstrate a self-correction when the corresponding hip configuration is brought into greater balance.

Figure 13-4n: Internal body type.

In time, your body will adapt to the intense demand of the wide-angle pose. By listening to your body and by becoming sensitive to your capacity for expansion, your body will change in ways that are quite pleasurable. The ultimate version of the pose was shown in figure 13-4j. It is only by moving slowly and by not allowing your body to shorten that you can achieve this lengthening and openness. In other words, you will get better results by releasing gradually. If your spine shortens in the wide-angle pose, it moves back. If your intention is to move your spine forward, then you will certainly notice when your spine moves in the opposite direction. This is something you can feel, providing you move slowly. Move only as your body opens. When you come to a spot of resistance, pause to allow for a softening. Then move farther by taking up the slack. This is considerably more effective than pushing against the resistance, which would only cause your body to contract and would not be worth the loss of integrity to your structure.

The wide-angle pose is a powerful yoga asana that can produce significant change. It is often intense, because the adductors and the pelvic floor are reluctant to lengthen, especially in the beginning. In time, the release of and relief from chronic holding in this area will make the effort worthwhile. When I first began practicing this particular pose in the early 1970s, I cried like a baby *while doing the pose* as my body flushed out layers and layers of emotional pain that had been stored in my pelvis. I haven't experienced that initial intensity again. This is analogous to the Rolfing process, in which the client's body is often considerably more sensitive to touch at the beginning of the work than during subsequent sessions.

Your body will show you where the tension is. The degree to which it has stiffened throughout the years may surprise you. Do not despair. Give yourself permission to explore openings in your body that you did not know existed. Asking yourself not to guard and protect yourself in ways that have become familiar to you is risky. But your body will change. In time you will experience healing and positive personal change and feel the sense of accomplishment that comes with being able to release into a yoga asana that was previously off limits to your body. In this particular stretch, because the pelvic floor can be so full of emotional and psychological material as well as physical obstructions, the newfound ability to open and release can affect you on several levels of functioning: sexual, emotional, and interpersonal. When layers of stored tension are released from your pelvis, there is an almost inevitable shift in your self-expression, including movement. The unique ways your body changes depend on the nature of the blocks, and the personal history that is stored inside your body.

2
0
3

SESSION FIVE

This Rolfing hour is the halfway point. Perhaps it is no accident, then, that the primary focus is on the center of the body. The fifth hour deals with the psoas, the pelvic floor, the expansion of the ribs, and the balancing of the entire torso. The release of tension from the deep chest, abdominal, and pelvic muscles is frequently the type of change that catapults the client into an increased body awareness and ability to produce positive change in his life. The fifth hour is a "core" session. When the work is deep, the corresponding release is deep. And the client has the opportunity to allow the personal change to be equally profound. If the Rolfer effectively teaches the client about the changes and releases that occur on the core level of the structure, the client is more apt to internalize these changes, integrate them into the fabric of his life, and make them long lasting and self-perpetuating. Following up the results and releases that occur in the fifth hour with stretching, breath work, and movement work will further ensure that the changes will be permanent.

Much of the fifth hour work takes place in the area around the heart chakra, or heart center. Many people think of the heart chakra as a patch on the front of the body. Consider that it is, in fact, the space between the front and back of the body, at the level of the heart. The back, then, is as much a part of the heart chakra as the chest is. Your chest may appear to be extremely open, but if the shoulders are being squeezed in the back, perhaps *because of an effort to force an opening in the* front, then the energy is just as blocked as if the chest itself were collapsed and closed. In the fifth hour, the true heart center is asked to open. For some, this entails more letting go in the front of the body; for others, the opposite is true. Whether you are dealing with pinched shoulders or a collapsed chest, the goal is to achieve balance between the front and the back. Optimal functioning, physical as well as energetic, can occur here.

PSOAS STRETCH

Lie on your back, with your legs, bent at the knees, dangling over the end of a bed or couch. Select a piece of furniture that is fairly firm and high enough from the floor so that your feet do not touch when your legs relax. (A Rolfing or massage table works well.) Your thighs and hips are horizontal. Let your legs hang. (See figure 13-5a.) Allow your lower back to rest, so that you feel comfortable and relaxed. You may find that your back is not in fact perfectly comfortable at first. This is not necessarily an intense stretch, but if your back does not easily accommodate itself to this position, give yourself several moments to breath and focus on letting go before you abandon the stretch altogether. Bringing your knees up to your chest may enable you to achieve the desired release in your lower back. Then, when you re-extend your hips, be conscious about continuing to allow your back to remain at rest on the bed. *You have given the tension away: Don't take it back.* Eventually, you allow your body to release a piece of tension, possibly chronic tension.

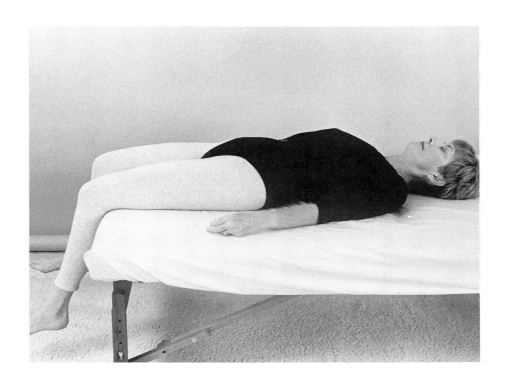

Figure 13-5a: Lie on your back with your legs, bent at the knees, dangling over the end of a bed, or a couch.

Once you are reasonably comfortable, bring one knee to your chest. Concentrate on giving the weight of your back over to the surface on which you are lying. *Do not contract the front of your body to meet your leg halfway.* Your thigh comes toward your chest, not vice versa. (See figure 13-5b.) Allow your body to remain at rest on the table by letting your leg float down to your rib cage. If you pulled your leg down, you would shorten your hip flexors, thus tightening the front of your body and inhibiting the lengthening across your back. Remember the Inner Angle. Put as much attention into the leg that is still dangling over the end as in the other one. The flexion of the first leg (at the hip joint), simultaneous with the extension plus the stretch of the leg that is down implies a deep release low into the abdomen. This stretch has important functional and postural implications.

The psoas muscle is called the "walking muscle." Your body can move efficiently indeed if the forward leg can flex deeply and effortlessly while the extended leg remains at rest. Stay with the first side, all the while breathing and feeling your body lengthen from the inside. Placing a sandbag or having a friend put a little weight on the extended leg might be particularly useful. This deepens the stretch between the origin and the insertion of the psoas muscle. It also increases the demand by flexing one hip while extending through the other. Repeat the entire series on the other side.

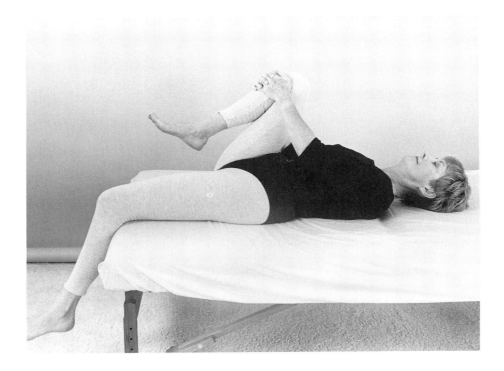

Figure 13-5b: Bring one knee to your chest. Concentrate on giving the weight of your back over to the surface on which you are lying.

BENT-KNEE LUNGE

Kneel on the floor, preferably on a soft surface, especially if your knees need extra padding. Place the left foot approximately two feet in front of the right knee. Bring both hips forward, dropping deeply at the left hip. (See figure 13-5c.) The right side will stretch from the iliac crest (top of the hip) to the insertion of the thigh muscles at the knee. Be aware of your spine moving toward the ceiling, without shortening the back muscles or lifting the back itself. Drop your weight into your hips, as you shift your weight forward. You can rest your hands over the front knee, but be careful to keep the shoulders soft and down. Repeat on the other side.

Figure 13-5c: One foot forward, one knee back, stretch the hips forward.

The principle of deeply flexing one hip while stretching the other back in extension is the same in the psoas stretch and the bent-knee lunge. By creating distance between the hips and the ribs (in the front, on the back, and through the center), your body gains the necessary space to maximize efficiency in walking, breathing, sitting, and standing. After these two stretches, walk around a bit. Notice where your body has more length. See if it is, in fact, easier to sit, stand, and walk with more room in your body, more expansion. You may feel less of an urge to shorten yourself right through the center of your body. The fifth Rolfing hour and the stretches presented here have an important and exciting benefit: When you cue your body to relax, it lengthens rather than collapses.

SESSION SIX

The sixth hour in the Rolfing series is typically back work. Aligning and releasing the back frequently require considerable work. Symbolically, the back side of the body represents the subconscious. It is the part we can't see, often hidden from our view. Functionally and structurally, there is almost always some issue to be addressed in the sixth hour. Most people have had some kind of back injury or experienced mild or acute back tension at some point. At least half of the people who want to be Rolfed or want to learn yoga are looking for relief from back pain.

The back must be viewed in relation to the front of the body. The back is the back of the front, and the front is the front of the back. You can't move the front of your body separately from the back. Although you are relatively static while vertical, movement runs through the back if the front repositions, and vice versa. (See figure 13-6a.) If your back gets hurt, your front will definitely be affected. In advanced bodywork classes, a student learns to look at the front of his partner's body to help solve riddles about pain and dysfunction on his partner's back side. For this reason, sixth-hour work often includes lengthening the quadriceps, stretching around the sternum, and softening the abdomen. Many people learn to manage their back problems successfully once they become more aware of the relationship between the front and back sides of their bodies. What is called "back pain", may actually be a structural or muscular problem that lies closer to the middle of the body.

For example, a person with low back pain may find that he is much more comfortable in his body, particularly his back, when he softens his belly or decompresses under his diaphragm. This is true especially if the tightness in the belly and under the diaphragm occurred originally because of an attempt to protect the back. A person usually protects his back, or guards his back, in such a way as to immobilize that part of his body. Except perhaps in certain acute situations, this immobilization is not effective. In order for your body to feel free, it needs to move freely. You can't learn to move freely if you aren't moving at all!

Figure 13-6a: Movement runs through the back if the front repositions, and vice versa.

Just as the front affects the back, the converse is also true. For example, lifting the chest and rib cage (that is, shortening the back) to correct round shoulders and to relieve midscapular pain can cause problems in the back. Holding onto *anything* (tensing a part of your body on purpose) as a solution to a structural problem is, at best, a Band-Aid effect, with one holding pattern simply replacing another. At worst, the compensatory response sooner or later exacerbates the original problem.

In the sixth hour my client and I work together to resolve alignment problems in the back, particularly as they relate to the rest of the structure. Any yoga asanas designed to open or stretch the back should factor in the same considerations. A forward bend done with the front of the body held tight will prevent the back from lengthening. Think of the spine as the midpoint between the front and back sides of your body. Both aspects of the spine— anterior *and* posterior—need to lengthen in order for the body to maintain its alignment in the yoga stretch. The ultimate goal of a simple forward bend, namely to open the back side of the body, is compromised if the front of the body does not open as well. (See figure 13-6b and figure 13-6c for the correction.) Learning how your body shortens or twists when you bend forward is valuable. With this information, your body can move past previous barriers by giving up its holding patterns.

Figure 13-6b: The ultimate goal of a simple forward bend, namely to open the back side of the body, is compromised if the front of the body does not open accordingly.

Figure 13-6c: When the front softens and lengthens, the back is able to open.

MODIFIED DOG POSE

Consider the modified dog pose as a warm-up to the dog pose; it is an easier version of the ultimate asana. By placing a lesser demand on your body, you can probably let your muscles lengthen with less effort, which in itself has its advantages. The purpose in both versions is to lengthen the front and back sides of the body from the inside. Your back lengthens by virtue of softening and opening at the core level, the place where the front and back meet. This dovetails with the values of relationship between back and front.

For the modified dog pose, place your hands on the wall about shoulder width apart, approximately shoulder height from the wall to the floor. *Once you place your hands on the wall, do not let them move.* This is the only way to ensure that you get an even stretch through your left and right sides. Place your feet on the floor, hip distance apart, about three or four feet from the wall (depending on your height) and equidistant from the wall. Press your hands into the wall. Bend your knees slightly. Lengthen your back so that your spine moves into the middle of the room. Move your shoulders down toward your hips (don't scrunch your shoulders toward your ears). *Breathe.* (See figure 13-6d.)

The objective is to fully extend your spine. To accomplish this, the tension is released on the front and back aspects of the spine simultaneously. The way to correct any structural or muscular holding patterns in your back is to lengthen your spine and the attendant muscular and tendinous attachments to the maximum. Technically, the longest position in your spine can occur with the vertebrae in full extension, allowing for natural curves in the cervical (neck), thoracic (upper back), and lumbar (lower back) vertebrae. This is opposed to hyperextended or flexed positions. Any time your spine migrates toward either of these two positions, especially in a chronic fixation, you lose the optimal lengthening on one side of the body. If your spine perpetually hyperextends, you lose the suppleness of the posterior compartment. In this case, the extensors (muscles along the back) are prone to contract.

Figure 13-6d: Hands to the wall, shoulder height. Feet hip distance apart. Stretch the spine. Allow the back of the legs to lengthen.

Likewise, when your spine is flexed forward, the spinal flexors (muscles on the front of the spine) are prone to contract. In a fully organized body, the flexors can lengthen even when the spine itself flexes. Likewise, the extensors can lengthen even when the body hyperextends. This is ideal, and this is where you are headed. If you are attempting these asanas for the first time, however, be patient as your body evolves and your movements gradually become more congruent with your intention.

The dog pose and the modified dog pose can open your body in places where you didn't even know you were holding tension. Depending on where your body tends to store tension, you might feel the stretch in your shoulders, your back, your hips, or the backs of your legs. Your body needs to learn to accommodate itself to the movement wherever you feel it.

In this particular stretch, attend to the unique needs of your pelvis. If you are inclined to hyperextension in your back (a sway-back), then make it a point to lengthen your spine, especially around the lumbar vertebrae. Avoid getting your back stuck in hyperextension. In terms of your back muscles, there is more length in extension than in hyperextension. Dr. Rolf used to say that total extension equals total relaxation. Concentrate in order to release the tension around the lumbar region and the sacrum. Technically speaking, your muscles around your tailbone lift toward the ceiling in hyperextension, or your lumbars push toward the floor (or both) in this particular stretch. If this describes you, move your tailbone more toward the wall behind you to lengthen your spine. If the muscles of the lower back are hard, with the spine embedded deep into the muscle tissue, this is another indication that your spine has gotten caught in hyperextension. Have a friend (or your Rolfer) palpate your back muscles to give you information on where you may still be shortening the musculature. This will help you know where and how to move toward maximum length. The spine lengthens from the pelvis to the first cervical vertebra in the dog pose. (See figure 13-6e.)

If your spine is inclined the opposite way—that is, if your lumbar vertebrae have migrated posteriorly and if they have a "tucked under" look—then your body has different needs in this stretch. Lumbar vertebrae pushing through the muscle tissue indicate that the tightness and the shortness are on the front of the spine or in your hamstrings (or both), and this is where you need to lengthen. In this case, roll your sitting bones and tailbone toward the ceiling. This will cause your pelvis to rotate fully, thereby lengthening the front of the spine and the hamstrings and taking the spine itself into complete extension. This will create the maximum length in your spine. The stretch in your hamstrings allows for another correction to the tightness across the lumbars. This is another example of "two ends to the same pattern." In this case, the tightness you perceive in two different body parts during a particular stretch indicates that both areas are connected to the same holding pattern.

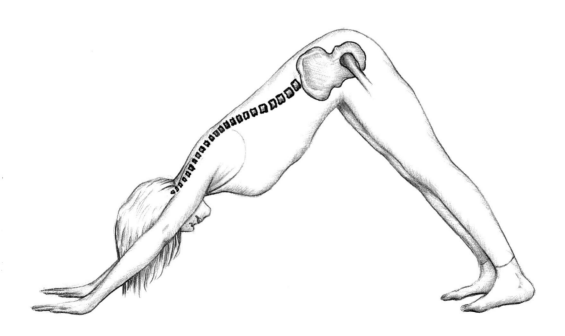

Figure 13-6e: In the dog pose the spine lengthens as the hips roll toward the ceiling. Allow the hamstrings to fully stretch.

Be sure your spine is moving away from the wall. The model in figure 13-6f intended to lengthen her spine, yet you can see how she actually shortens it midway in the pose. As she lengthens the front of her body, her back opens. (See figure 13-6g.) If your upper back tends to push upward, focus your attention on softening and dropping your chest, lengthening under your arms, and changing the angle of your rib cage.

Figure 13-6f: The shortness on the front of the spine prevents the back of the spine from lengthening.

Figure 13-6g: In a forward bend, the stretch moves through from the front to the back.

Discussing the subtleties of this extremely valuable yoga pose is worthwhile. Many individuals have corrected substantial structural blocks in their bodies by diligently working in this stretch. In conjunction with the sixth Rolfing hour, or by itself, the modified dog pose has the potential to produce lasting and important change, especially if you practice it on a regular basis.

DOG POSE

The final version of this yoga asana places a much greater demand on your hamstrings, because your hands are on the floor and you have to bend over much farther to reach it. Your hips have to rotate more because the floor is a greater distance away than the wall was in the previous stretch.

Begin with your hands on the floor, against the wall, still shoulder width apart. Turn your thumbs in and your fingers out. The web between your thumb and index finger faces the wall and presses down into the floor. (See figure 13-6h.) Much of the strength and support necessary for a good dog pose comes from the contact of this part of your hand with the floor. With your hands turned out like this, your shoulders are "prerotated." In the pose, roll your shoulders away from your ears, lengthening the trapezius and directing your spine to extend. This will also help you to create the desired length from your hands, through your arms, across your chest and belly, and along the entire back side of your body, including your hips, hamstrings, calves, and Achilles tendons. This is an "all- purpose" pose.

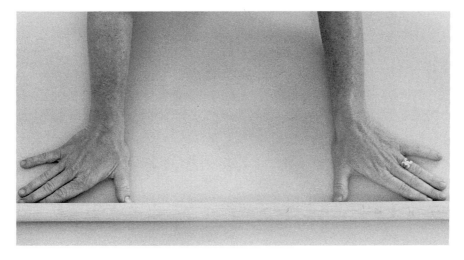

Figure 13-6h: Place your hands next to the wall, thumbs in, fingers out.

Push with your hands against the floor. Let the stretch move through your arms and shoulders. Your spine lifts toward the ceiling, giving your body a sense of length and lightness. Use your hip muscles to lift your buttocks toward the ceiling. Sometimes it helps to bend your knees just a little or to come onto your toes (or both). These two adjustments take some of the pressure off the backs of your legs, thus enabling you to get a fuller rotation to your pelvis. Meanwhile, as your spine slowly begins to lift, your heels drop. This creates a dynamic stretch in your legs (with the two ends moving in opposite directions).

Remember, everything is connected. You are continuously looking for information from your body. Where is the tightness? What pulls you away from the direction toward which you want to move your body? Where does the energy get hung up? Where are the weaknesses and strengths in your body?

Gradually straighten your knees and drop down into your heels. Your legs will slowly adjust in response to the intense stretch across your back. Despite the intensity, allowing your heels to drop onto the floor in the dog pose can feel wonderful. If it is more intense than it is pleasurable, with time this will change. The opening to your calves comes as a great relief. When you release the tension through your legs, the Earth seems to rise up to support you. (See figure 13-6i.)

Notice the difference between allowing your heels to drop into the ground and pushing your heels down. By allowing gravity to guide your heels down, you manage to lengthen the Achilles tendons without putting undue strain on the anterior compartments of your lower legs. Remember, if your heels *drop* down, there is no effort, strain, or tightness in the legs. The feet are very important in the dog pose. If they are not dropping down toward the floor, that is, if the heels are lifted up or pressed down, it is because of the relative shortness in the leg and feet muscles and because of the rotations of the bones. By releasing tension through the legs and feet, you are enabling your body to stretch and lengthen from the base upward.

Figure 13-6i: The dog pose is a full-body stretch, from the wrists to the hips, and down the back of the legs to the heels. Be aware of both aspects of the spine,

Reread the special considerations regarding the lumbar spine in the description of the modified dog pose. Keep in mind this same goal of lengthening and extending through the lumbars as well as the thoracics. The object is to avoid getting stuck in hyperextension or flexion of the vertebral column.

HIP ROTATOR STRETCH

The position of the hip rotators influences the general alignment and suppleness of the entire back side of your body. I spend quite a bit of time in the sixth hour loosening and balancing the area around the sacrum, hip joints, and coccyx (tailbone). (See figure 13-6j.) The hip rotators attach to these bones and determine how the entire pelvis moves, or doesn't move.

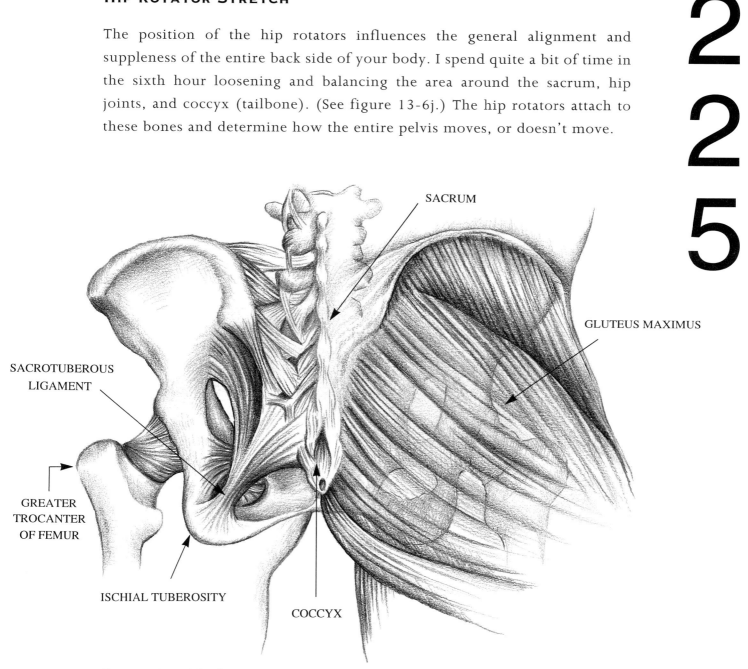

Figure 13-6j: The hip rotators move the sacrum, hip joints, and coccyx.

Sit with your right leg crossed under you so that your right foot is tucked in as close to your left buttock as possible. Cross your left leg over your right thigh, with your left foot tucked close to your right buttock. If your body does not look like that of the model in figure 13-6k, do not despair. Many people do not have naturally loose buttocks or hips. You may adopt a simpler position, using a pillow to support the hip of the bent leg. (See figure 13-6l.)

Figure 13-6k: Cross your left leg over your right thigh, with your left foot tucked close to your right buttock.

Figure 13-6l: It's easier to bring the top foot further away from the bottom hip. A pillow provides additional support.

Resting your head in line with your spine, place your hands on the floor about a foot beyond your knees. (See figure 13-6m.) Now the entire back surface of your body is being stretched. This movement forward helps to emphasize the release to your hip and buttock muscles. Gradually, as your back lengthens and your buttocks soften, you can lower your torso down over your top leg. (See figure 13-6n.) Eventually, you may be able to rest your chin on your top knee.

Figure 13-6m: Resting your head in line with your spine, place your hands on the floor about a foot beyond your knees. Feel the length across your back, as your hips sink into the floor.

Figure 13-6n: Gradually, as your back lengthens and your buttocks soften, you can lower your torso down over your top leg.

As your hips yield to the demand of the stretch, close your eyes and sink into the floor. Pay attention as you ask your body to expand and release, allowing the floor to support you. Be sure to release any squeezing in the floor of your pelvis, the area around the perineum. Observe the strength in your arms as they support your body in lengthening toward the ceiling. Allow a deep release to move into any area where you perceive some holding. Send your breath into these parts. Repeat on the other side. The intensity of this stretch will lessen in time as you develop more strength and balance. Likewise, the dog pose eventually will become more pleasurable.

SESSION SEVEN

In the seventh Rolfing session, you learn to rest your head comfortably on top of your body. This is, perhaps, the ultimate in mind–body connection. Ideally, by having had the neck, head, and shoulders worked on during a portion of each of the earlier sessions, you have already prepared the body to support the head being on top. A primary goal for each person who goes through the Rolfing series is to have an appropriate relationship among the head, the neck, and the underlying structures. This particular goal is so important partly because the head can rest on top only when the rest of the body has regained its alignment. A successful seventh hour, with the head comfortably at rest on the top, is a reflection of the positive changes that have occurred throughout the entire structure during the earlier sessions.

Dr. Rolf explained that the verticalness of the human body is a measure of our evolution as a species. We are moving away from the body type with the head at the front end of a relatively horizontal spine, as was characteristic of our earliest ancestors, who were quadrupeds. The spine must be vertical before the head can rest on top. In terms of personal development, this is one of the most compelling arguments for the potential to evolve that becomes available through Rolfing.

This particular goal is something that takes time to accomplish. The head cannot be put on top in one session. It gradually moves toward this position in response to a number of changes and releases that happen below. The housebuilder goes through many painstaking measurements and takes many steps before building a satisfactory foundation. The foundation takes into account the shape, weight, and size of the structures to be balanced above. Many considerations must be factored in before the final plan is executed. In the same way, I deal with a number of other problems before solving this particular one. For example, the head will not rest on top if the knees are pressed back hard in hyperextension. The backward motion of the knees will inevitably result in the forward motion of another body part—for example, the hips—to counterbalance the knees. The body is trying to establish its own internal balance by pushing and pulling its way to an off-balance but mock vertical position. The head cannot rest above such a compromised structure, because the structure itself is not stable, just as a shaky foundation will not adequately support a building.

Because of the nature of compensations, the various parts of a body that is attempting to compensate are arranged in a random fashion. Therefore bodies that have been pulled and pushed out of alignment and off the vertical axis vary greatly. A pair of shoulders that are lifted up, for example, are not symmetrical. An essential element of a holding pattern of this type is that the body parts, the shoulders in this case, are not balanced.

There are eight layers of connective tissue between the outer skin and the intrinsic muscles of the cervical vertebrae. Effective head and neck work must be deep enough to balance and release the superficial as well as the deep muscles. A full range of motion of the neck depends ultimately on the organization of deep muscles and tendons that cross the vertebrae, the jaw hinge, and the occipital region.

Achieving complete range of motion in the neck requires that the head be on top of the body. Many professionals overlook this fact and fail to see the connection among the head, the neck, and the rest of the body. If the body is pitched forward, held back, twisted, or foreshortened in some way, the tension invariably travels up through the spine to the head and neck region. From a mechanical and structural viewpoint, this is inevitable. If the head tends to live behind the center of gravity, it stays there because of a series of distortions in the body, combined with tension in the neck.

Chronic tension and complete range of motion are mutually exclusive. If the head is in a chronically or acutely fixed position, the head and neck naturally lose some of their ability to move through a thorough and complete range by virtue of the shortened areas in the connective and muscle tissue. For a complete range of motion throughout the entire body, all of the muscles that surround a joint must be able to lengthen as the relative position of the bones that cross the joint changes. If the muscles and their tendinous attachments are foreshortened, this phenomenon cannot occur. The idea of the Inner Angle, as presented in chapter 10, will help you in understanding how to release the holding in your body that you discover through the yoga stretches.

Many people can *hold* their heads on top. But doing so misses the point and is contrary to the goal of Rolfing. Ideally, our heads *rest* on top. This comes from deep integration of the underlying structure and a balance of the major components that add up to good posture. The goal, then, is to allow our heads to comfortably and effortlessly rest on top. In Rolfing, we often refer to the head as *floating* on top.

When doing the following exercises, keep in mind that the neck and head are connected to the body below. In each movement sequence, see if you can isolate the stretching and lengthening in the neck and head, so that the rest of your body does not work hard while the neck tries to relax. For example, while you do the rotations, notice if you squeeze anywhere else in your body. If you squeeze your buttocks, you have compromised the complete fluidity of the head and neck. Notice your chest, your shoulders, your arms, and your upper back. The release from the head and neck comes from deep inside your body. With practice, you can feel the connection from your neck all the way through your body and into your feet. When this happen, you will know you have effected a complete release.

CERVICAL ROTATIONS

Sit or stand comfortably with your spine stacked, each vertebra resting on top of the one below. If you are standing, look in a mirror, or work with a friend to discover any ways in which your body pushes or pulls off the vertical axis. How can you release these pushes and pulls so that your body becomes more balanced? Here is a hint: The anterior and posterior movement means that something has tightened, pulled, or shortened. *That is the only way for your body to get off the vertical axis.* The more your body lengthens, the more nearly it follows the vertical axis. Your ideal posture is a position in which you lengthen by releasing. "Holding yourself" in "perfect posture" is an oxymoron. This message has been repeated because of the importance for your mind to understand that in this process you are not learning how to hold yourself. What may seem like splitting hairs, or getting hung up on semantics, is actually an important clarification, and one that enables your mind, including your thought processes, to work harmoniously with your body.

Focus on your breathing as you sense the position of your head. Upon exhalation, drop your right ear down to your right shoulder. Soften the muscles of your right shoulder (Inner Angle). In other words, do not bring your shoulder to your ear. Your head still faces straight ahead: Do not tilt your face toward your shoulder. (See figure 13-7a.)

Isolate the stretch, and release on the left side of your neck. Allow the right side of your neck to fold softly, like an accordion. Can you tell the difference between *pulling* your head to the right and *dropping* your head to the right? When you pull, your body gets the message to contract something: in this case, the right side of your neck. When you cue your neck to drop to the right, you are more apt to keep the muscles soft. Again, the concept of the Inner Angle will help you understand this. Also, as you drop your head to the right, keep the space open in the right waistline. The right side of your body maintains its neutrality and its length even as your head drops to that side. Except for the cervical region, the rest of your spine remains vertical. This movement allows you to isolate the stretch in your neck.

Figure 13-7a: Drop your right ear down to your right shoulder. Do not bring your shoulder to your ear.

After about a minute, bring your head down and forward until you feel a gentle stretch across the upper back and between the shoulders. The same ideas apply here. The front of your neck and throat remain soft as your head is gently lowered down to your chest. (See figure 13-7b.) The rest of your body remains vertical, so that your center of gravity is not disturbed even with your head forward. Isolate the stretch across the back of your neck. If you pitch your weight forward, you may unwittingly favor the back of your neck, especially if stretching it is uncomfortable, intense, or even just unfamiliar.

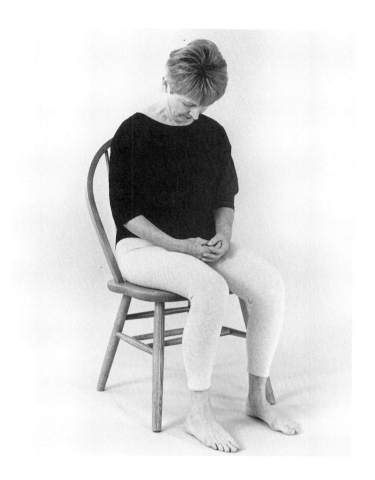

Figure 13-7b: Roll your head forward until you feel a gentle stretch across your upper back and shoulders. Your neck and throat remain soft.

Release here for about a minute; then gently roll your head to the left. Follow the directions for moving your head to the right, switching each instruction to the opposite side. Rest and relax in this position; then allow your head to fall to the back. Each movement is a slow, deliberate, large, sweeping motion; make sure to achieve the full range of motion of the muscles and bones of the cervical spine. Concentrate on keeping the back of your neck soft as you allow the front to lengthen. Gravity is perfectly capable of lowering your head down. (See figure 13-7c.)

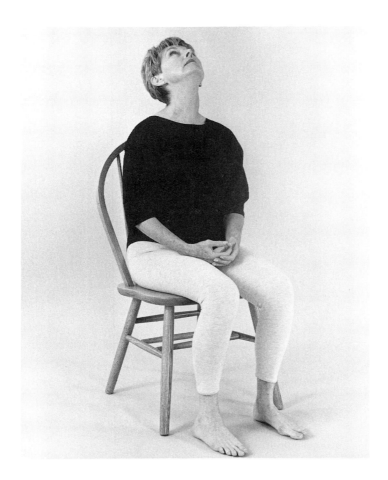

Figure 13-7c: Allow your head to fall to the back. Your shoulders and the back of your neck remain soft.

The more you drop your shoulders down, the more room you have to allow your neck to fall to the back. The trapezius muscle has a variety of functions on both sides. One is to elevate the shoulders. Another is to hyperextend the back of the neck. This large muscle covers a lot of territory. (See figure 13-7d.) If the muscle fibers responsible for elevating the scapulae are contracted, then the shoulders will be raised. This greatly increases the chances for compressing the back of the neck in the hyperextended position. When the head drops back, it has less room to move if the shoulders are raised. Also, contraction of one portion of the trapezius greatly increases the chances of contractions of other portions of the trapezius. This is one simple reason why shoulder and neck tension tend to go together. For the purpose of this stretch, dropping and softening your shoulders, will ease and lengthen the back of your neck, and give both more room to move. When the entire trapezius softens, your neck can drop back more easily without shortening or tightening.

After dropping your head back, slowly return to your left side. Continue now in the opposite direction, repeating the previous instructions. After you have completed the rotation in both paths, return your head to the upright position and imagine it floating on top of your body. Close your eyes and be with the sensation of your head untethered from the muscles that lie below it. Because your stretching has produced a deep relaxation, your head can now be on top with considerably less effort.

Chest-and-Arm Stretch

As we are continually reminded in yoga and Rolfing, all of our body parts are connected on a structural level. The old song about the hip bone being connected to the leg bone is quite accurate. A Rolfer sees the body as a series of relationships. When a Rolfer says that everything is connected, she means it—literally and figuratively. Typically, if a client goes to a massage therapist because of neck tension, the massage therapist will rub and knead the neck to help bring relief.

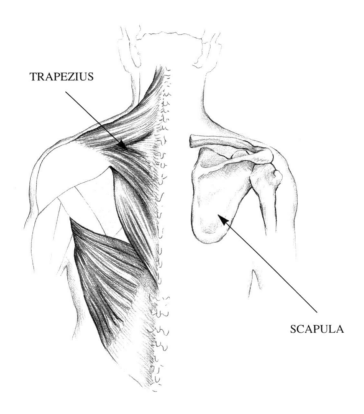

TRAPEZIUS

SCAPULA

Figure 13-7d: The trapezius muscle elevates the scapula and hyperextends the back of the neck.

If the same individual presents neck problems to a Rolfer, the Rolfer will examine the client's body to see how the neck problem is related to other structural or functional problems throughout the client's body. If I were the Rolfer in this case, I might decide that I could obtain the best results by modifying the angle of the ribs with relation to the lumbar spine. If this resulted in a more stable and aligned spine that provided the necessary support for the head and neck, the client might find relief from symptoms in a way far more dramatic than from a more "direct" method. Rolfing is holistic in that the entire body is taken into consideration. In this case, the circuitous route is more effective than the more direct route, especially with regard to the long-term benefits.

Discomfort, pain, and dysfunction are the results of aberrations and disruptions in the body. Headaches, neck pain, jaw tension, and even eye strain do not exist in a vacuum. Often tension or structural permutations occur elsewhere as well. Head, neck, and jaw problems are connected to problems in the scapulae, the arms, the entire rib cage, and the spinal column.

The following stretch is designed to balance the head by substantially opening the underlying structures. Let your arms be lifted until you feel a stretch across the front of your chest and deep in the front of the shoulders. (See figure 13-7e.) Work with a partner who is holding a stick. Your hands should be approximately shoulder width apart or closer. The closer your hands are, the more intense the stretch to the front of your chest and shoulders. The more flexible you are, the easier it is to allow your arms to be lifted. Working with a partner is ideal, because you don't have to shorten (work) your muscles to produce the stretch. And if your body is relatively passive and at rest, relaxing and lengthening will be easier. Keep dropping the weight of your arms so that your partner is lifting you. Help your partner by softening your body.

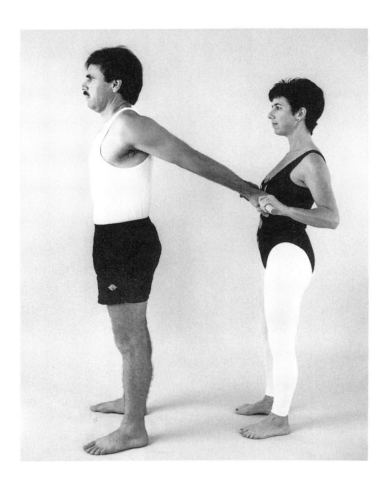

Figure 13-7e: Let your arms be lifted until you feel a stretch across the front of your chest and deep in the front of the shoulders

Stretch only as far as you can without shortening in your neck or pitching your head or torso forward. Either one of these compensations would be a way to lift your arms, but you would accomplish this lift without isolating or releasing through the shoulder joints.

If the shoulders are loose and supple, the arms can actually lift toward the top of the head. (See figure 13-7f.) Just as with cervical rotations, it is important to isolate the movement in your arms and shoulders. If you feel your body tightening anywhere, stop and release before you attempt to bring your arms higher. As your arms and shoulders gradually let go, your partner takes up the slack by lifting the stick, a little bit at a time.

Figure 13-7f: If the shoulders are loose and supple, the arms can actually lift toward the top of the head.

You can achieve approximately the same effect as the stretch just described while practicing on your own. Kneel in front of a sofa, a chair, or some firm surface of comparable height. Interlace your fingers or take hold of two ends of a towel. Bring your hands as close together as you can. Roll your shoulders down, away from your ears. *You must get a complete external rotation of both arms in order to achieve this downward movement of your scapulae.* (See figure 13-7g.) The area immediately in front of the glenohumeral joint must widen in order to accommodate this fairly intense stretch across the front of the chest. (See figure 13-7h.) Concentrate on relaxing the trapezius. This enables your shoulders to drop down which gives more room to the back of your neck.

Figure 13-7g: Kneel in front of a heavy piece of furniture. Stretch your arms back, allowing a opening across the front of the chest and the shoulder joints.

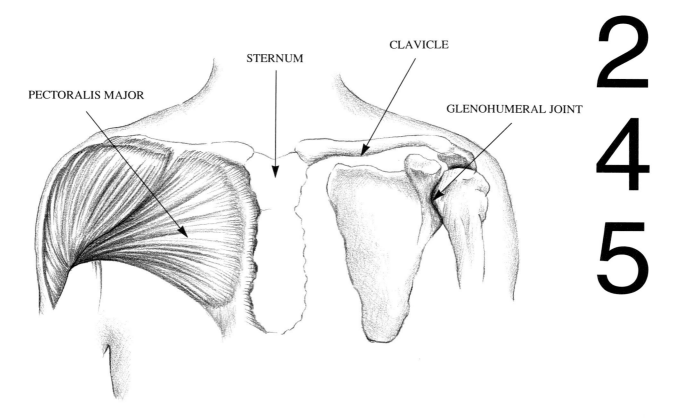

Figure 13-7h: The glenohumeral joint and the front of the chest open in these stretches.

As you breathe and release with this stretch, notice what happens to your rib cage. Avoid pitching your body forward. (See figure 13-7i.) If you intend to lengthen your body and isolate the stretch in the shoulder girdle, avoid shortening and compensating there. Your shoulders are supposed to move down in this pose. Shoulders moving up feel different from shoulders moving down. Be aware of how your body moves. Learn to identify the feelings associated with various stretches, as well as various ways of holding. Gradually allow your movement to become congruent with your intention.

Figure 13-7i: Avoid pitching your body forward. Isolate the stretch across the front. Do not allow the ribs to compress down. Do not let your head press forward.

Any shortness of the deep or superficial fascial planes on the front of your body will make it harder to produce a rolling down of the backs of the shoulders. Here you can have a direct experience of the relationship between the back and the front of your body. Something amazing occurs as you release across the front. Your head slowly approximates the top position, with fewer and fewer pulls forward and back. When you establish this dynamic movement between the front and back, your head has nowhere to go but up!

CAMEL POSE

This series requires slightly more flexibility, but the benefits make it worth your time to learn to stretch your body in the following ways. Begin by placing your hips against the wall. Your knees are on a mat or the floor, hip distance apart. Place your hands on the wall at approximately shoulder height and shoulder width. (See figure 13-7j.) Think of your back lengthening as you move the front of your body, from the hips to the chest, up the wall. Your shoulders do not lift. Using the wall to stabilize your hips, gradually stretch your upper back in two directions simultaneously: to the ceiling and back toward your heels. If you think of lengthening your spine, there will be less of a chance that you will scrunch your back. Your head is the last to come back. Your head comes back only when the front has lengthened to its maximum potential. (See figure 13-7k.). Your neck muscles in this stretch become the Inner Angle. The back of your neck folds softly like an accordion as your head falls back gently. Actually, gravity takes your head back. (See figure 13-7l.) As in the previous series, your shoulders roll down. This movement enables your chest and upper back to get the maximum release.

Ultimately, you can practice this stretch away from the wall. Without the wall stabilizing your hips, you may find that you can stretch your hips even farther forward. The increased distance between your hips and your heels allows for an even greater stretch through both the front and back of your spine. (See figure 13-7m.)

Figure 13-7j: Place your hips against the wall. Your back lengthens as you stretch the front of your body up the wall.

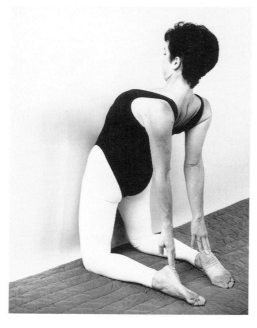

Figure 13-7k: As your back lengthens up and back, your hands come closer to your feet. Your head is the last to come back.

Figure 13-7l: Your head comes back only when the front has completely stretched. Let gravity take your head back.

Figure 13-7m: The front lengthens as the back softens. By bringing your hips forward, there is more room for your spine to stretch.

As you practice these stretches, you will begin to discover more relaxation in your neck, chest, shoulders, and upper back. By balancing the underlying structures, you make it easier to relax and release any holding in the neck, in the jaw, and even in the cranium. In addition, what was once a difficult or uncomfortable pose gradually becomes easier and more natural for your body. This is a strong argument for practicing the poses, even if they are not particularly pleasant at first. The ability of your arms to lift easily and comfortably on the table (for example, in the chest-and-arm stretch) is positive evidence that you have released a chunk of chronic tightness from your body. Your body has become more supple, simultaneous with becoming more aligned and balanced. This is one of the most exciting and valuable aspects of yoga. The positive feedback unequivocally demonstrates that your body has let go of something that previously caused some kind of disturbance, discomfort, or limitation. When a difficult pose becomes more pleasurable, you have done something wonderful for your body by letting go of old, usually undesirable habits and patterns of holding.

SESSIONS EIGHT AND NINE

The objectives of the eighth and ninth Rolfing sessions vary according to the unique needs of the individual client. Typically, I look at my client's body to determine where the energy gets hung up when he moves. As he walks across the room, where is there a lack of movement in his body? Where does the integration of the body appear to be lacking? In the eighth hour, we may determine that the upper body is relatively less integrated than the lower body, or vice versa, or that the upper body lacks support from the lower body, or vice versa. Depending on the answers to complicated questions and other considerations, I will structure the time to bring movement, integration, and support to the body where it appears to be most lacking.

The following stretches are full-body releases: The entire body is given the chance to self-adjust and make head-to-toe corrections. This is true in all asanas, but particularly so in this group. If you are well into the Rolfing series, then your body is ready to respond at this level. Likewise, if you have taken your time learning the asanas in sessions 1 through 7 in this book, you are prepared to observe and release tension in bigger waves that move through your body. When you first begin truly living in your body, changes occur in smaller pieces. Perhaps at first you drop your shoulders down, or soften your knees, or unclench your buttocks. As your body gets more and more integrated, you notice tension in patterns. That is when, while in the asanas, you shift from noticing and releasing local tension to handling the larger networks of stress and holding in the connective and muscular tissue. With practice, you can directly experience a release from your heels to your jaws.

Notice what kind of sensations you feel in your body. See if your body seems tighter from the waist up or from the waist down. If you were to take a snapshot of both parts, from the inside, how would these two images compare? Perhaps the unique way in which your body stores tension is a left–right phenomenon rather than an upper–lower type of pattern. Answering these questions may give you some insight into how you organize yourself around your Line. These are the same questions your Rolfer asks as she decides the best course to follow in working with you on your body.

These asanas are designed to reveal the larger patterns of muscular and fascial tension. Keep your mind open to the bits of information that add up to a greater understanding of and appreciation for your unique body. In terms of your evolution, you will find it easier to change if you understand and accept yourself as you are. By knowing in advance that the yoga asanas can reveal to you insights about yourself, you will be more apt to receive this information without judging yourself for what you find. Countless times I have felt myself—as well as observed my students—make important discoveries about meanings that had lain beneath layers of habitual holding. Recently a client told me after doing a simple forward bend that she was having flashbacks of all of the deeply negative messages her mother had given her about her body. She had learned to hold her body rigid to please her mother and to protect herself from her mother's invasiveness and cruelty and had been doing this for many years. Sometimes, as in this case, people are blessed with clear insights that explain questions from their past. Other times, release is more general. It feels emotional and may be accompanied by tears but has a less specific content associated with it. We can never force these releases. Their occurrence is a gift.

One way to focus even more on the emotional quality and benefit of serious stretching is to stay in present time while doing the asanas. The yoga asanas are more likely to touch and affect your psyche and spirit if you focus on your body, your emotions, and your breathing while you stretch. One of the difficulties that people have while doing yoga, as well as when they get worked on, is that they tend to split off from the experience. This occurs for a variety of reasons. First, people in our culture tend to believe that we should be productive every waking moment. An individual who thinks this way may find it hard to surrender his mind to the task at hand, namely, to strengthen, relax, and balance the physical body and to rest and quiet the mind. If a person has not decided beforehand that the time spent on yoga is valuable and worthwhile, he will have a greater tendency to split off. I encourage my students to regard whatever time they spend stretching—even if it is only for five minutes—as just as valuable as anything else they do that day. Focusing your mind on your body multiplies the benefits of the yoga stretches.

People also split off into their minds while doing yoga because the information that presents itself—indeed, the experience itself of stretching chronic tension—can be so intense that they can't bear to stay present. I see people whine and act out like recalcitrant children when doing a simple forward bend. Naturally, stretching chronic tension is intense. This intensity eases when you focus on it with the idea of consciously releasing it, or of simply exploring it. Provided you are not stressing your body by demanding too much of it, your willingness to consciously explore how you are holding your body tight is an important step toward a positive change. By this time in your yoga practice, it should be second nature to you to pay attention in order to make conscious changes. When you hold your breath and send your thoughts far away, you probably avoid the feelings in your body, *thus reducing your own ability to release tension deliberately.*

TRIANGLE POSE

Stand with your feet about three-and-one-half to four feet apart, depending on your height. Initially, your feet, legs, and hips face forward. In fact, your entire body is equidistant from the wall you are facing. Then, without disturbing your hips, turn your right leg and foot out. Turn your left leg and foot in. With your hands, feel where your hips are. Rotating your femur (thigh bone) in the hip joint is different from rotating your entire pelvis. Part of the benefit of this pose comes from your ability to distinguish this move and to isolate the rotation in your leg bones.

Stretch your arms to shoulder height. By lengthening equally across the front of your chest and your upper back, you have created a lateral expansion to your body in which the front and back open equally. Soften your shoulders and widen between the scapulae (shoulder blades). On a full exhalation, stretch your torso to the right, toward the turned-out leg and foot. Your hips shift to the left. Do not bend forward at the hips. This is a lateral stretch. Throughout the entire stretch, both legs remain straight at the knee: not locked, just straight. Be aware that the bottoms of both feet remain in contact with the floor. Because your feet are resting on the floor, you have the balance and flexibility to move from the base upward.

The upper arm stretches toward the ceiling as the lower hand rests lightly on the floor behind the right foot. As an alternative, depending on your flexibility, you can rest your right hand lightly on your lower leg, above the ankle. This requires less of a stretch than placing your hand on the floor. Roll the bottom ribs forward and the top ribs back. Make as much distance between the scapulae as possible. Allow your neck to remain in line with the rest of your spine. Do not let the front of your body or your head come forward. (See figure 13-8/9a.)

Figure 13-8/9a: Feet are about 3 1/2 feet apart. Hips move to the left as your spine moves to the right. Bring your left arm to the ceiling.

What are you most aware of in this stretch? What information does your body give you? Where does the release need to occur? Can you allow the stretch to move throughout your entire body? Stay in the stretch for about a minute. On a deep exhalation, come up slowly. Repeat the stretch on the other side.

Technical note to Rolfers and other bodywork therapists: The triangle pose is an excellent exercise to help release the tension associated with a nonvertical spine deviated from a scoliotic (lateral S) curve. Observe how the spine in Figure 13-8/9b is being stretched. The intrinsic muscles close to the transverse process of the vertebrae, as well as the larger, more superficial extrinsic muscles, are lengthened in this pose in a way that would not happen in a person's normal routine. *One of the reasons why our bodies stay stuck is that our movement patterns tend to avoid taking us directly into our holding patterns.* Either we manage to keep from feeling the tightness in our bodies, or we never ask our bodies to move in ways that are unfamiliar.

Side bends and scoliotic curves in the spine can be addressed by balancing and lengthening the muscle groups and connective tissue throughout the body that play a role in this particular aberration. The triangle pose places a specific demand on the spine that challenges the holding around a variety of spinal fixations, including side bending. Determine to which side the spine is bent. The student does the pose away from that side first, and then to the other side, and then to the first side again. The stretch often brings relief from the discomfort associated with deviations in the spine and the concomitant tension in the musculature.

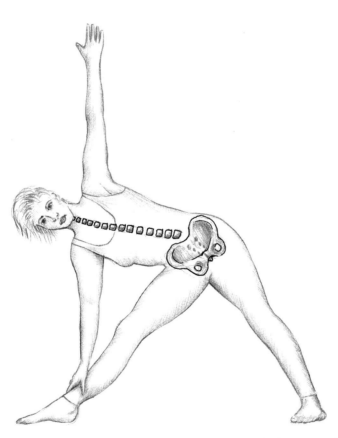

Figure 13-8/9b: The stretch in the spine can help move through habitual holding patterns, including the tension associated with scoliosis.

MODIFIED TRIANGLE POSE

With the upper hand, turn the thumb side back, rotating the entire arm and shoulder up and around to the back. Get as deep a release as you can through the front of the shoulder joint. When you release here, your arm can stretch back and around. Bring your fingers around to the front of the back leg. (See figure 13-8/9c.) This variation gives a deeper stretch to the front of your torso. If you have difficulty bringing the arm around, focus on dropping the shoulder of that arm down in the back. Relaxing the trapezius on that side will give that arm and shoulder considerably more flexibility. As you rotate your head toward the ceiling, continue to roll that shoulder away from your ear. The distance between your head and your shoulder gives your neck the necessary range of motion to rotate while in this position. As an easier alternative, bring the upper arm around to take hold of a belt placed around the inside of the leg being stretched. (See figure 13-8/9d.) Leotards and workout clothes make excellent handholds.

Figure 13-8/9c: Get as deep a release as you can through the front of the shoulder joint as you bring your upper hand around to the opposite hip.

Figure 13-8/9d: A belt around the front hip may be easier to reach with the top hand.

CROCODILE SERIES, PART 1

I call this series the M. D. R. (Minimal Daily Requirement) of yoga. If I spend about fifteen minutes doing these stretches in the evening before I go to bed, I can handle and release most if not all of the tension that has accumulated in my body during the day. This is truly a full-body stretch. As a bonus, the crocodile pose develops abdominal strength. As with all poses, do not hurry through this. The real value comes from your giving your body time to relax. Because of the demands to stretch your hamstrings in this pose, you may want to hang over in a forward bend or rest your legs up against a wall to stretch your hamstrings first. This is particularly true if the backs of your legs are prone to tightness.

Lie on your back on the floor. Be sure you have plenty of room on both sides. Rest your arms in a **T** position on the floor, in line with your shoulders. After a long inhalation, exhale and lift your legs straight toward the ceiling, bending at the hips, keeping your knees straight. Focus on your belly as the source of strength to hold your legs 90 degrees from the floor. (See figure 13-8/9e.) By relaxing your arms, throat, neck, and chest, the contraction is isolated in the abdominal muscles. This is called "selective contraction." In yoga, this means that you relax the muscles not needed to perform a particular feat (the parasitic muscles) while consciously contracting where the strength is required. In this way, your body avoids unnecessary tension and fatigue. While working part of your body in the poses, you maximize the flow of energy to muscle tissue elsewhere in your body, where there is no demand to contract.

Figure 13-8/9e: Focus on your belly as the source of strength to hold your legs 90 degrees from the floor. Rest your back on the floor.

If raising your legs straight is too difficult, bend your knees. If it is still too difficult, use a belt over the bottoms of your feet to provide the necessary support for your legs. (See figure 13-8/9f.) Bring your legs 90 degrees from the floor, stretching your heels toward the ceiling. The support of the belt around your feet may enable you to release your hips, bringing your legs to a full right angle. As your hips open, you can gradually take hold of your feet, but only while your shoulders rest back on the floor. (See figure 13-8/9g.)

Figure 13-8/9f: Use a belt over the bottoms of your feet to provide the necessary support for your legs. Rest your shoulders on the floor.

Figure 13-8/9g: As your hips open, you can gradually take hold of your feet, but only while your shoulders rest back on the floor.

Swing both hips slightly to your right. Turn both feet toward your left hand. With both legs straight, lower your feet slowly, with control, and place them as close to your left hand as possible. Use your left hand to hold onto the belt. Bring your feet as close to shoulder height as possible. (See figure 13-8/9h.) If your feet crash down to the floor, do not despair. With regular practice, your abdominal muscles will develop to the point where you can control the placement of your legs and feet on the floor next to your hand. This will come as your abdominal muscles strengthen and your hips and hamstrings lengthen. You are now lying down on the left side of your hip and leg. By stretching your right shoulder down and rolling your right hip up, you have created a beautiful rotation throughout your entire spine. Let your head turn to the right to complete the twist. (In a completed yoga twist, the head turns in the opposite direction from the sacrum, with the entire spine lengthening and twisting.) You are stretching tiny, intrinsic muscles that are close to the vertebrae, ones that are unlikely to get stretched in your normal daily routine. *Breathe!* Consciously allow the top half of your body, including your head and neck, to rotate and relax to the right, while the bottom half of your body rotates and relaxes to the left. If you can, send a full, relaxing breath to your belly. This will enable you to complete the release right through your center.

Figure 13-8/9h: With both legs straight, lower them as close as you can to the opposite arm, which is on the floor at shoulder height. Use the belt to reach your feet with your hand.

Continue to stretch the backs of your legs. Ideally, you will eventually be able to take hold of your big toes with your right hand. (See figure 13-8/9i.) Stay in the pose for at least a minute or longer. Remember, you are not *holding* in the stretch, you are *releasing* in the stretch. This yoga stretch provides much information. Allow the pieces of body awareness that become available to flood your mind. Notice the *patterns* of holding. What is the connection between the tension that you perceive in the left shoulder, for example, and that patch of tightness on the right medial thigh? By releasing the tension, how does your body become better organized? Where do you observe your body not being supported by the floor? What happens as you become aware of the holding here?

Figure 13-8/9i: Eventually you will be able to take hold of your big toes with the hand lying next to your feet.

When you feel that your body has shifted into a position of deep release and greater comfort, swing your legs up again. Pause in the center before swinging your hips to the right and rotating your legs to the left. At first, you may need to bend your legs to accomplish this. Eventually, both legs will remain straight. Repeat the directions with your feet and legs moving toward your left hand.

One of the primary purposes of each stretch is to allow your body to release tension. Substantial physiological and structural changes do not happen in an instant. Many people make the mistake of doing yoga poses for as long as they can *hold on*. Each pose should be done for as long as you can *let go*. Finding that you have lost track of time in a pose is a remarkable experience. When your awareness is filled with the sensations of your body surrendering and opening up, there is no drudgery in the stretch. Pleasure and spiritual rhapsody overshadow the intensity.

CROCODILE SERIES, PART 2

Allow yourself a few long, relaxing breaths after completing part 1. Focus on permitting your body to be fully supported by the floor. Then flex the right hip and lift the straight leg toward the ceiling, at approximately a right angle to the floor. As you stretch the right leg, allow the left leg to remain at rest on the floor. As the release moves through the pelvis floor, the flexion of the right side does not disturb or shorten the left side.

Either take hold of your big toe or lasso a belt over the bottom of your left foot. As your arms reach toward your left foot, your upper back and shoulders remain at rest on the floor. Take about a minute in this initial stretch to allow your body to expand. Expansion in this case is synonymous with accepting the support of gravity.

Take hold of both ends of the belt with your left hand. Or keep holding onto your left foot with your left hand. Rotate your entire left leg out, pointing your left foot out past your left shoulder. While you concentrate on allowing your right leg and hip to remain at rest on the floor, slowly lower your left leg out to the left at a diagonal. The release moves through both halves of your pelvis. Stretch your left arm out as close to your left foot as possible. Do not bend your left arm, as doing so would prevent your left shoulder from enjoying the stretch as well. (See figure 13-8/9j.)

Figure 13-8/9j: Lower your left leg out to the left at a diagonal. Bring your foot as close to your hand as possible. Allow the opposite leg and hip to remain at rest on the floor.

Once your left leg is on the floor—or close to the floor, resting on a pillow if necessary—let a wave of release move throughout your entire body. The obvious stretch is in the medial compartment of your left leg. The more subtle yet more important stretch is in the fascial plane throughout your entire body. Give yourself at least a minute to release into the stretch and observe the information that your body is presenting to you.

The next phase is to bring your left leg back up to the center. Then gradually lower it down as you lengthen through your left hip. Raise your right leg straight up. Take hold of both ends of the belt with your left hand, or hold onto your right big toe with your left hand. This time, turn your right leg out at a diagonal to your left. While resting your right arm out like a T on the floor, move your right leg to the left, toward and past your left shoulder. Naturally, depending on your flexibility, you will bring your right foot as close as you can manage upward along your left side. You have to turn completely onto your left hip to do this. The rotation in your spine is a result of your upper torso moving to the right while your pelvis moves to the left. The upper, inner left thigh, close to your perineum, becomes the Inner Angle. Release any squeezing between your thighs. Your left buttock softens on the floor (or you notice how you squeeze there) as you continue to rest more and more of your left side down into the floor. Turn your head to the right so the rotation goes through your entire spine. (See figure 13-8/9k.) Take many big breaths that move throughout your entire body. Gently direct the breaths into the areas where you perceive the need to release pressure or tension. Continuously give your weight over to the floor.

269

Figure 13-8/9k: Turn on to your left hip. Bring your right leg at a diagonal across to your left hand. Soften your upper inner left thigh and buttock on the floor.

When you come back to the center, take time to observe the sensations associated with having moved energy into areas that were blocked. What changes do you observe from side to side in your body? How has the shape of your breath and your capacity for breath changed? Rest comfortably for a moment before repeating the series with your right leg. At the completion of the entire series, observe what happens when you cue your body to rest on the floor. Learning to relax your body at will is one of the most marvelous benefits of yoga. When you let gravity and the floor hold your body, holding yourself becomes superfluous.

SESSION TEN

Savasana is the pose of complete relaxation. This pose complements the tenth Rolfing hour, the purpose of which is to establish a homogeneousness and connectedness throughout the entire musculature and fascial network in your body. In my Rolfing training, one of my teachers remarked that the Rolfer faces her karma in the tenth hour. Any soft tissue in the client's body that has not released comes up for review in the last session. Likewise, in savasana, the yoga student finds that any muscles that are still holding on become noticeable. Because your body is enjoying a heightened relaxation, any remaining patch of tension is felt as a disturbance in the overall flow of energy. It is more difficult to notice specific areas of holding when most of your body is tense. In savasana, the contrast enables you to identify and release whatever has not been surrendered during the previous series of yoga stretches. Frequently a person becomes aware of the tension in his chest, for example, only after he releases the tension in his abdomen and shoulders.

Savasana is frequently referred to as the most difficult of all yoga asanas, because it asks you to relax completely. It is called the "corpse pose" in some yoga books. This term, however, is a misnomer: Your body in savasana in no way resembles a corpse. On the contrary, it throbs with aliveness. During savasana, you take the time to enjoy the benefits of having stretched, balanced, and strengthen your body during the previous asanas.

Many individuals, especially athletes, find it is easier to do a full-arm balance (handstand) for sixty seconds than to relax completely for even a fraction of a moment. In savasana, your mind becomes flooded with sensations from your entire body. In order for this to occur, your mind must disengage itself from the thoughts to which it is normally attached. These thoughts are often distractions. Learning to quiet your mind is an invaluable skill. To truly take charge of your body, you must learn to consciously release tension on an ongoing basis by switching your mental focus from thoughts to sensations.

In savasana, you learn to focus your attention on the areas where there is some disruption to the overall flow of energy in your body. For example, if you are dealing with a chronic knee pain, you can assume that there is some structural imbalance between the femur (thigh bone) and the tibia and fibula (lower leg bones). Through the yoga asanas, you have probably released a significant portion of the muscle tension that was associated with the knee soreness. People often describe this experience as one of feeling more connected with the leg that had the problem. This feeling of connectedness helps a person then pinpoint any leftover areas of disturbance.

Savasana helps resolve structural problems. With your body horizontal on a comfortable, supportive surface, the potential for structural change is great. Any spots where you are holding your body tense become obvious. If your legs are habitually rotated, for instance, relaxing on a supportive, horizontal surface will enable you, eventually, to feel how the muscles used to rotate your legs are contracted. Using the heavy–light model described in chapter 10, you can see the various ways in which you either lift your body up off the floor or press your body into the floor. Either way, you resist the support of gravity through the unique ways your body has learned to hold tension. In savasana, gravity is no longer merely a theoretical notion. The more you experience gravity *directly*, the more you can maximize the potential for energy to flow throughout your entire body.

Savasana is often taught with props, pillows, and bolsters. I do not favor this method. If your body is lying on a firm, comfortable, horizontal surface (such as the floor with a yoga mat) you get invaluable feedback from your body in terms of discovering areas of tension and shortness. For example, if your back is not comfortable during savasana, your structure is probably rotated in some manner or has some area of compensation. Your body is not at rest. By putting a pillow under your back, you are favoring the compensation. Your back may benefit from the opportunity to find the floor, to surrender to the inevitable tug of gravity without a pillow. I do not feel that you *must* avoid using props during savasana. Simply be aware of the therapeutic value of ultimately resting and feeling comfortable on a completely horizontal surface.

Remember, relaxing takes time. Rushing through savasana is a contradiction in terms. You can easily spend ten minutes or more with the following guided relaxation. If a friend reads the instructions, he can select other body parts to focus on, while using the same format of suggestions. The following is a guideline, and can easily be embellished upon. There is nothing fixed in a process of this kind: It lends itself to creativity and imagination. The magic of savasana is that it teaches you to become familiar with the tension so that you understand how you hold yourself before you make a change. This becomes practice for living in your body with more consciousness and skillfulness.

GUIDED RELAXATION

Lie comfortably on your back. Make any adjustments in your body that stretch you out and help you feel more at ease. You may find it helpful to move your shoulders down away from your ears and widen them away from each other. Let your arms rest by your side. Experiment with turning your palms upward toward the ceiling. Now turn your palms down. Which is more comfortable? (Pause) Which position brings more openness and possibly more stretch to your shoulders? (Pause) In which position is it easier to relax from your neck and shoulders, through your arms, down into your hands? (Pause) In which position does your breath flow more fully? When you have found a comfortable position for your arms, let them become completely still. Allow them to rest next to your body. Allow the natural weight of your arms to make contact with the floor.

Now become aware of your pelvis, legs, and feet. Is the lower half of your body perfectly comfortable, or do you need to make an adjustment? Is this position ideal, or do you need to shift slightly? You are looking for a position in which your body can naturally relax, a position in which you feel *supported*. You can relax only when you perceive this as something safe to do. Sometimes what prevents your body from relaxing is a strong emotion, such as fear, held in the musculature. This emotion, then, is associated with letting go and will be re-experienced as you *relax in spite of the emotion*. As you allow your body to be supported by the floor, holding yourself becomes superfluous. The floor holds your body, including your emotional body, for you.

Observe your breath. Notice if your breathing becomes deeper or more shallow as you experiment with various leg positions. Allow yourself to become completely comfortable. When you have found the ideal position for your hips and legs, allow your body to become completely still from the waist down.

Shift your attention to include the upper and lower halves of your body. Have you indeed allowed your body to become still, or is there still some activity in your musculature? If you cue your body to rest on the floor, what do you notice? Let your attention move to the area in your body where there may still be some activity. Continue to cue yourself to drop into more and more stillness. Allow a deep, calming wave to move throughout your entire body.

Again, notice the stillness in your body. Beyond the beating of your heart, the gentle rise and fall of your chest with each inhalation and exhalation, and the movement of the blood coursing through your entire circulatory system, your body has become quiet and motionless. Notice the shift in your musculature toward greater relaxation. How does your weight change when you relax? Do you observe your body getting lighter or heavier on the floor? Notice *how* you allow your muscles to relax. Do you stop pushing down, or do you stop lifting up? How does the energy pattern change in your body when you allow yourself to relax? (See figure 13-10a)

Figure 13-10a: When you let gravity and the floor hold you, it becomes superfluous to hold yourself. Savasana is the pose of complete surrender.

Allow your attention to move to any part of your body where there may be a tiny patch of tension. It may feel like a major or minor disruption to the energy flowing in your entire body. It may be a large chunk of holding in your back, or something smaller, such as tightness behind your knees. Without disturbing the stillness in your body, allow your attention to focus on the area where you perceive some tension. Do not hurry to make a change. Experience the value in discovering precisely how you store tension in your body. As you take a few breaths, observe whether a shift occurs.

Allow yourself to discover precisely what you are doing in this area where you perceive tension. Are you squeezing, lifting, pushing, or contracting your body? Is more of your natural weight on the floor, or less? Allow yourself to become familiar with precisely how you have put pressure in this particular body part. What are you doing? How have you allowed the energy in this area of your body to become separate from that in the rest of your body? Let yourself make these observations. In this process, *the time you spend paying attention to the particulars of your holding patterns is valuable.* Can you become fascinated by how you hold tension in your body? If you find an area where there is some tension, become even more still and quiet there. In the stillness, you learn how you have placed tension in your body. Get a good sense of what you do and how you do it before attempting to make a change.

In the stillness of your body, the next change occurs as you consciously allow the tension to melt. By discovering just how you squeeze your buttocks, or wherever you have noticed the holding, you enable yourself to become more effective at releasing the tension on your own. The more you practice this, the more adept you become at moving energy and relaxation into body parts that have been blocked or tight. Do not be discouraged if you do not move easily from noticing the holding to releasing it. Be patient with yourself. The more time you spend observing the precise feelings associated with holding on, the better you will learn to let go.

As you make these observations, pay attention to the ways in which you slowly release the tension from your body. As you relax, see what you do and how you do it. What unsqueezes? What drops down? What softens? What ceases to bear down into the floor? How do you allow your body to move into a position of increased relaxation and with increased energy flow? Observe carefully how you let the tension go.

When you have released a chunk of tension in your body, become aware of the stillness again. Enjoy the sensation of energy and relaxation moving into body parts that had been blocked. Send your breath into these parts. Out of the stillness, and as a direct result of feeling a part of your body open up, you will naturally notice the next area that needs your attention. The energy in this area will feel blocked, unlike the energy in most of the rest of your body.

At this point, you may wish to review these instructions. Allow your intuition to tell you when to move on. As you practice going through this unwinding and unwrapping, you will develop a good sense of when this cycle of release is complete. Often a deep breath, a sense of settling down, or a noticeable wave of release moves through your body. These signs indicate that the cycle is complete. There is no end point to deep relaxation, rather a deepening of the process. The releasing doesn't stop: It becomes more subtle.

CLOSURE

Now your body has shifted into a position of even greater stillness and quietness. You can feel your body completely at rest on the floor. Feeling the natural weight of your body on the floor is an indication that structural and soft tissue corrections have been made. Only when you pull, twist, or shorten internally does your relationship to gravity change. As you rest your body on the floor, the support that you allow yourself to experience becomes a powerful catalyst for releasing deep holding. There may be a swelling in your emotional body as you receive this support. The floor now holds your body:

You do not need to hold yourself. Having "fallen," you are still safe. Having let go, nothing bad has happened.

Can you notice your body having reowned and reintegrated the body parts that were previously tense? Observe your legs and how they are connected with your pelvis. What do you observe in the connection between your feet, through your legs, and into your hips? Is the energy fluid and undisrupted? Or is there a break, a rough spot, or a dull spot in the energy flow from your pelvis to your feet? If there is, notice it. This may be an area where you have more work to do.

What is the connection from your shoulders, through your arms, into your hands? If you could take a snapshot of the energy pattern in your entire upper body, what would you see? Are your torso and arms connected energetically, or is there a break? Notice what is happening in your upper body. Can you allow your body to be still and at rest?

As you breathe, can you bring all the parts of your body into relationship? Can you allow your breath to move into every imaginable square inch of your body? From the top of your head, down your face, through your throat, and into your shoulders, can you open yourself to a connection deep in the inside, close to your core? Allow that energy to move into your chest, as well as your upper back, and to fill up the space between the two. Take several enormous breaths that fill you from front to back.

Now allow this energy flow to move into your belly, connecting the front and the back of your body. When your breath moves from your abdomen into your lower back, you can feel how your body comes together on the inside.

This same breath moves slowly from your belly and back into your pelvis. Watch your breath as it swirls around your hips, around your buttocks, and into your genitals. Notice both buttocks. Can you feel the natural weight of your body move through your hips into the floor? Can you feel the softness of the back side of your body as you rest comfortably? If you feel any discomfort whatsoever, can you expand that part of your body, thus giving more of yourself over to gravity? What is it like to surrender so completely?

Allow your legs to become connected, through your pelvis, to the rest of your body. As you permit your breath to go beyond your pelvis, into your legs, how does your awareness of your body shift? As the energy of your pelvis travels down to include your upper and lower legs and your feet, can you surrender your body even more? Can you allow yourself to continuously shift to deeper and deeper levels of relaxation? Can you open yourself to greater and greater levels of energy flowing throughout your body? Can you give yourself permission to have a body that is both relaxed and energized at the same time? This is a good time to lie quietly as you take about five huge breaths, in and out, deepening your surrender to gravity.

Know that you will be moving soon. Without disturbing your restfulness on the floor, imagine some of the activities in which you will be engaged today. Continuing to feel supported on the floor, can you see yourself going throughout your day in a heightened state of body awareness and expansiveness? Is there an activity coming up in your day that, in the past, was strenuous or stressful? An activity in which you found yourself, in the past, contracting? Now, while maintaining the support you feel on the floor, envision yourself responding to the same event in a new way. Now your breath flows, and the energy continues to move through your calm and relaxed body. Take a risk. Allow yourself to stay open. Sense how you do this.

When you move, know that you are going to take your relaxation and body awareness with you. Before you get up, take some huge breaths that connect the top of your head to the bottoms of your feet—and everything in between. Notice how long it takes for you to take a completely full breath when your body is this relaxed and this open. Can you take several breaths as if you had all the time in the world to breathe? Notice how much energy there is in such a deep breath. What else do you observe about your full breath?

Before you get up, slowly roll over onto your side. Bend your knees. Rest for as long as you need before you slowly come to a sitting position. With each movement, ask yourself to stay connected on the inside. Moment by moment, give the tension away. Be with the sensations and notice the feedback your body gives you as you gradually return to the world beyond your own body.

SAVASANA, A SKILL BUILDER

Just as I use my hands to make a clean sweep through my client's body in the tenth Rolfing hour, your consciousness of the sensations in your structure, of your musculature, of your breathing and of your overall energy flow does the same thing in savasana. With each passing minute, your body sinks deeper and deeper into profound relaxation. The unique thing about this state of relaxation is that you are not drifting toward sleep. Many people find it a new experience to lie horizontally, while comfortable, relaxed, and warm, and while keeping their minds quiet and alert. This position is normally associated with sleep. One of the differences between sleep and savasana is the crisp focus of the mind on the body, with the noise level in the mind itself dropping to an imperceptible decibel.

In sleep, we do not necessarily relax the tension in our bodies, and this can lead to unpleasant side effects. Fatigue and muscle soreness are two common problems that some individuals face in the morning. For a person who does not rest his physical body—who maintains a rigidity in his musculature—a long night's sleep may not be good enough. Savasana is ideal for practicing the skills that help make sleep a more relaxing and thus more rejuvenating event. In fact, because your body may relax more in savasana than it does while you sleep, savasana can provide as much, if not more, rest. It is common for newcomers to yoga, and to Rolfing for that matter, to report an instant improvement in the quality and depth of their nighttime sleep. This improvement is a direct result of having released more physical tension *before* going to bed.

Depending on many factors, you can have any of a wide variety of experiences in savasana. On some days, you can become completely absorbed in noticing and releasing tension. This is a wonderful process that leaves you feeling incredibly energized and refreshed. Many people are surprised by how much zest they feel after savasana. If you relax substantial amounts of tension, you will feel less tired and rundown. *Moving about requires considerably less effort when your body is free of tension.* One of my students calls savasana a power nap.

On the other hand, if you are suffering from long-term exhaustion, you can have the opposite sensation in savasana, that is, you may want to sleep for hours. In the same way, many people feel a tremendous need to sleep after a Rolfing session. It may sound amusing, but all that letting go can be a lot of work! This scenario is especially true for individuals who are exhausted but who never slow down long enough to let themselves actually feel how tired they are. The particular way they hold tension enables them to keep going, to push forward (literally), overriding any messages from the body that it needs sleep. When such an individual truly rests in his body, when he lets down the guard that has hidden the need for rest, the exhaustion can seem overwhelming.

Frequently in savasana the mind attaches itself to issues from earlier in the day or to current pressures in life. Naturally, the more you are dealing with, the more there is to let go of, to detach yourself from. Regardless of the details of your life, savasana is an excellent opportunity to turn the tides of stress and tension back, to give yourself a break from the pressures in your body and the demands on your mind. The more mental chatter that you experience during savasana, the more difficult it is for you to focus on the relaxation. But when you can switch from noticing the inside of your head to noticing the feelings in your body, that in itself helps to quiet the mind. In this case, savasana is truly a meditation, the object of which is your physical body.

One of my students has been taking yoga classes for approximately eight years. He is a businessman who keeps himself very active mentally. Often he finds it difficult to relax. Months ago, he told me that his mind never quiets during savasana. Just recently, he had a real breakthrough. Although he was quiet when he told me this, I could tell by his face and his body how happy he felt. That evening in class, he reported, he had had a spiritual experience during savasana: His mind had become remarkably quiet. After eight years, his "practice" was paying off.

For many of you, the experience of this man is naturally attainable. Yoga, including savasana, has the potential to radically alter your experience in your body, indeed your experience of your Self. Dr. Rolf said frequently that Rolfing is a vehicle for transformation and evolution. Yoga is the same. Whether the result is relaxation, body awareness, feeling more connected to the Earth, a spiritual awakening, structural alignment, or all of the preceding, yoga and Rolfing are well worth the time you spend learning to quiet your mind, focus on your body, and, ultimately, connect the two.

REFERENCES

283

Chapter 1. Rolfing and Yoga: Blending Two Disciplines

1. Deane Juhan, *Job's Body* (Barrytown, N.Y.: Station Hill Press, 1987), 341.

Chapter 4. Yoga: A New Twist

1. Mary Talbot, "Om is Where the Heart Is," *Newsweek* (Feb. 3, 1992), 71.
2. Elizabeth Fernandez, "Breathe Deeply: Yoga Has Gone Mainstream," *The San Francisco Chronicle* (Feb. 23, 1992), A-1 & A-10.
3. Dean Ornish, *Reversing Heart Disease* (New York: Random House, 1990), 143.
4. Ibid., 147.
5. Ibid., 142-143.
6. Swami Rama, Rudolph Ballentine, M.D., and Swami Ajaya, Ph.D., *Yoga and Psychotherapy: The Evolution of Consciousness* (Honesdale, Pa.: Himalayan International Institute of Yoga and Philosophy, 1976), 56.

Chapter 6. The Energy Body

1. Bernie Siegel, *Peace, Love, and Healing* (New York: Harper & Row, 1989), 16.

Chapter 7. Holding Up and Holding Down

1. Jack Lee Rosenberg, *Body, Self, and Soul: Sustaining Integration* (Atlanta, Ga.: Humanics Limited, 1985), 134.

Chapter 8. Levels of HoldingChapter

1. Deepak Chopra, *Ageless Body, Timeless Mind* (New York: Harmony Books, 1993), 39.

Chapter 12. Getting Started with Yoga

1. Vanda Scaravelli, *Awakening the Spine* (New York: HarperCollins, 1991), 139.

L

language 65, 67
latissimus dorsi 126, 127
layering 125, 202
learning 9
leg 26, 53, 55, 63, 88, 101, 137, 163, 169, 170, 274
leg, rotation of 171
leg-balancing pose 169
leg-balancing pose, variation 172
lengthen 140, 159, 163, 193, 213, 233
letting go xiii, xxiv, 7, 61, 65, 67, 74, 89, 90, 157, 205, 206
Levine, Dr. Peter 43
life force 72, 73
lifestyle x, 6, 15, 21, 48, 100
life-supporting decisions xviii, xix, 20
ligament 170
lightness 275
limitations 7
line of energy 156
line of tension 156
Line, Rolfing 116, 141, 252
love xvi, 6, 8, 53, 59, 60, 74, 75, 108
love, of self 123
low back pain 211
lower back 21, 63, 97, 99, 139, 166
lumbar curve 216
lumbar spine 40, 63
lumbar vertebrae 97, 101, 166, 200, 218, 224

M

Maharishi Mahesh Yogi 42
manipulation viii, xxi, 36, 43, 116, 120, 122, 125, 126, 156
medical model 103, 105, 109

medical technology viii
medicine ix, 18, 23, 29, 43, 49, 81, 82, 102, 103
medicine, allopathic 102
meditation xii, 48, 52, 282
memory 102, 104
mental health 51, 82
meridian xvii
metaphysics 72, 205
metatarsal 169
micromovement 29, 156, 186
migraine 51, 105
Mills, Stacy xii
mind, quieting of 280, 282
mind-body connection 9, 231
Mindell, Dr. Arnold 43
mobility 118
mobilization 128
model xv, 58, 59, 63, 99, 113
modified dog pose 215, 218, 221
modified triangle pose 257
molestation 27, 81
mountain pose 146
mountain pose, see tadasana 136, 137, 139, 141
mouth 92
movement viii, xxi, 13, 19, 24, 26, 32, 33, 55, 81, 91, 93, 111, 112, 116, 117, 118, 121, 124, 125, 129, 142, 146, 211, 212
movement instructors xx
movement therapy 118
movement, congruent 107
movement, deliberate 24
muscle xxi
muscle contraction, waste products of 126
muscles 124, 126
muscles, extrinsic 232, 256
muscles, intrinsic 139, 232, 256, 264

N

natural weight 65, 274, 276, 277, 278
neck 55, 92, 118, 156, 250
neck brace 32
neck problems xxiv, 24, 25, 28, 31, 241
neck rotation 118, 119
nervous habit 77
nervous system 77, 125
Newsweek 48
ninth Rolfing session 251
nourishment 81

O

objectives, Rolfing and yoga x
occiput 123, 232
optimal health viii, x, 20, 102
organization 136, 177, 183, 232
Ornish, Dr. Dean 48, 51
Orr, Leonard 42
oxygen 35, 38, 126

P

pacing 37
pain x, xii, xv, 8, 18, 19, 21, 22, 24, 25, 32, 36, 37, 44, 46, 49, 55, 75, 79, 81, 82, 96, 103, 159, 163
pain killer 32
parasitic muscle 117, 260
patella (see kneecap) 63
pattern 8, 27, 85, 86, 88, 137, 155, 177, 200, 266
pelvic blocks 92
pelvic floor 137, 183, 202
pelvis xiii, 26, 40, 90, 92, 101, 109, 110, 128, 129, 136, 137, 179, 183, 274, 278, 279

ABOUT THE AUTHOR

Rosie Spiegel is a leader in the field of body therapy, yoga, healing, and movement. She is an Advanced Certified Rolfer, and a graduate of the Iyengar Yoga Institute in San Francisco and of the Trager Institute in Mill Valley, California. She has traveled extensively in this country as well as throughout Europe and India, pursuing her studies in yoga and bodywork. Rosie has participated in several teacher training courses with B. K. S. Iyengar in Pune, India. As a practitioner and teacher in this field since 1972, Rosie brings a unique and rich combination of skills to her work.

Since 1986, Rosie has been on the teaching faculty in the Advanced Degree Program at the Body Therapy Center in Palo Alto, California. Rosie also teaches yoga, movement, and body therapy through the Rolf Institute in Boulder, Colorado, and in workshops throughout the country. She currently teaches yoga for the Pacific Athletic Club in Redwood City, California. Rosie is the author of *Yoga for Rolfers, Movement Teachers, and Their Clients*. She has also written numerous articles for *Yoga Journal*, *Runners' World*, *Journal for the American Massage Therapy Association*, and *Rolf Lines*.

As a dancer, yogi, and athlete for many years, Rosie brings her own embodiment and enthusiasm to her work. She maintains a private practice in San Carlos, California, where she lives with her husband, Larry, and their children, Frosty and Molly.